7.

The Social Science Program of the Mershon
Center for Education in National Security,
The Ohio State University: Pamphlet Series

NUMBER 2

January, 1966

OCEAN SCIENCES,

TECHNOLOGY, *and the*

FUTURE INTERNATIONAL LAW OF THE SEA

By William T. Burke

Ohio State University Press

PREVIOUSLY PUBLISHED

1. A Revaluation of Collective Security: The OAS in Action, *by Jerome Slater* $1.50

ACKNOWLEDGMENT

The author acknowledges support in aid of research and publication from the Mershon Center for Education in National Security of the Ohio State University, and from the Office of Research of the Ohio State University.

The author is grateful to the following for permission to quote from copyrighted material: Dr. J. W. Clark, author of "Methods and Techniques for Sea-Floor Tasks," which appeared in *Ocean Science and Engineering;* the Marine Technology Society, publishers of *Ocean Science and Engineering;* the International Oceanographic Foundation, publishers of *Sea Frontiers;* and the editor of the *American Behavioral Scientist.*

WILLIAM T. BURKE

College of Law
Ohio State University
September, 1965

CONTENTS

INTRODUCTION

In the two decades since World War II, the international law of the sea has undergone careful reconsideration. National officials involved in maintaining the public order of the oceans have devoted serious attention to assessment and revision of this venerable body of law. Representatives of various private groups that share a common involvement in ocean exploitation, though they pursue numerous diverse objectives, have added their substantial efforts in appraisal and recommendation. Contributions of the same character may also be seen in the observations of individuals acting in a private capacity. The culmination of this enhanced activity came in 1958 with the adoption, as suitable for the demands of mid-twentieth century society, of the four Geneva conventions on the law of the sea.[1]

Accompanying, and outlasting, this recent revival of concern about the flow of decisions regulating interactions on the oceans has been an even more intensive upsurge in scientific inquiry into the complexity of oceanic phenomena.[2] This apparently sudden

[1] 2 U.N. CONF. ON THE LAW OF THE SEA OFF. REC. 132–43 (U.N. DOC. No. A/C. 13/38 (1958).

[2] Speaking of the United States only, the Interagency Committee on Oceanography in 1963 noted "the recent growth in oceanography from a ten-million dollar enterprise involving only a few hundred professional workers in 1953 to one

emergence of interest in scientific exploration and technological development rests primarily, no doubt, upon awareness of the high military value of expansion in knowledge of the sea,[3] but there is, equally clearly, a widespread realization that the ocean offers tremendous opportunities for realizing a great variety of important benefits for all peoples.[4] For a quick introduction to the potentialities in, and possibilities of, ocean exploitation, the following brief excerpts from recent authoritative studies are illuminating. An early study prepared for the Foreign Relations Committee of the United States Senate observes:

> In recent years, oceanography has received a great deal of attention. One reason for this is that the ocean has an important impact on world climate. To understand the factors controlling the atmosphere, a much better understanding of the effect of water movements and of transfers of energy between the boundary of sea and air is needed. A second reason is the potential wealth of the oceans and the fact that a new oceanic technology may provide new foods and mineral resources to mankind. A third and very important reason is military.
>
> Technological and scientific advances now permit us to consider more realistically the possibility of exploration and exploitation of vast ocean resources. Among these the possibility of developing revolutionary new techniques in the maritime and submarine arts opens wide vistas. For example, with nuclear energy new marine developments are feasible that use high-energy input, operate for long periods without refueling, and have the ability to operate the propulsion machinery without oxygen. Other developments with new engines and new ship designs may greatly change marine transportation technology, particularly the uses of submarines for nonmilitary activities.[5]

More general indication of the vast potential benefit is to be found

---

thirteen-fold greater in 1963 pursued by a few thousand. . . ." ICO, OCEANOGRAPHY: THE TEN YEARS AHEAD, A LONG RANGE OCEANOGRAPHIC PLAN, 1963–72, 7 (ICO Pamp. No. 10, June, 1963).

[3] Committee on Science and Astronautics, OCEAN SCIENCES AND NATIONAL SECURITY, H. R. REP. No. 2078, 86th Cong., 2d Sess. 17 (1960).

[4] *Id.* at 22–24.

[5] Study by Stanford Research Institute for Senate Committee on Foreign Relations, *Possible Nonmilitary Scientific Developments and the Potential Impact on Foreign Policy Problems of the United States,* 86th Cong., 1st Sess. 23 (1959).

in the introduction to the National Oceanographic Program for the United States, as conceived by the Interagency Committee on Oceanography. Speaking of the need for long-range planning for oceanographic work, the ICO declared:

> Such planning is all the more important in terms of making most effective use of research resources when considering that oceanography is small with respect to some indices of its practical importance. The burgeoning world population, particularly in the underdeveloped areas, makes the oceans with their huge and inefficiently exploited food resources of inevitable and increasing value to humanity as a whole. . . .
>
> Other indices of the strategic importance of the oceans are becoming ever more clearly recognized. The cloak of concealment provided by a medium which is virtually opaque to all forms of energy except sound is of immense military significance. . . .
>
> Other aspects of the oceans affecting all or large numbers of us in common include the health hazard posed by pollution from industrial wastes such as oil, chemicals, sewage, etc. and from radioactive substances; danger to life and property from waves and flooding; risk to shipping from floating ice, storms and navigational hazards; and threats to resources such as the recreational value of the seas which should be common property.[6]

That technological conditions no longer present an overwhelming obstacle to extension of significant activities to all parts of the sea is evident from the following observations in a report prepared by Dr. Edward Wenk, Jr., for the Committee on Science and Astronautics of the United States House of Representatives:

> The barrier which has historically restrained man from submarine operations at all depths in the ocean now shows promise of being dissolved by technological advancement. High-strength steels, high-strength aluminum alloys, fiberglas reinforced plastic, titanium, and beryllium as engineering materials show the promise of producing structures whose strength-to-weight characteristics will permit their use in submarine hulls for operation 10 to 20 times deeper than the depth cited for the Nautilus. Exactly what will be the scientific as well as practical benefits are unpredictable, but recent experience has dramatically shown the advantage of priority in scientific achievement. Vehicles in increased number, either self-

[6] ICO Pamp. No. 10, *supra* note 2, at 4. See also HULL, THE BOUNTIFUL SEA, *passim* (1964).

buoyant as are submarines, or bottom crawlers, and even fixed underwater stations in which men may live and work safely, constitute some of the emerging realities that now make possible an attack on the entire ocean.[7]

Unfortunately, together with these optimistic accounts of realistically anticipated advantages are to be noted other statements indicating considerable disquiet about the legal arrangements established or available for permitting realization of the estimated gains. As early as 1959, even before the final failure at Geneva of the multilateral effort to resolve some critical international legal problems involving the sea, Dr. Columbus Iselin, a widely known American oceanographer, is reported to have expressed the judgment:

> The economic and social problems that will be encountered as we begin seriously to exploit marine resources seem to me to be formidable, much more formidable than the remaining unsolved scientific problems. Some very wise agency needs to be developing the ground rules within which the vast marine resources can be developed in an efficient and safe manner for the benefit of all mankind.[8]

And only six years after the considerable labors of eighty-seven nations at the 1958 Geneva Conference on the Law of the Sea and four years after the 1960 Geneva Conference on unfinished business of the same subject, Dr. Athelstan Spilhaus, dean of the Institute of Technology at the University of Minnesota, declared:

> We need, for example, a new look at the law of the sea as it relates to the emerging exploitation of mineral resources, aquaculture, and the uses of the sea to promote national economic well-being and strength.
> This is perhaps one of the most important and difficult of the marine problems to be tackled. Somehow we must bridge the dichotomy of preserving the traditional international freedom of the seas and making investment in the exploitation of the oceans feasible. It's an interesting thing that groups of distinguished

[7] H. R. Rep. No. 2078, 86th Cong., 2d Sess. 35–36. But see Groves, *Awake in the Deep*, 10 Sea Frontiers 285, 294 (1964).

[8] Quotation contained in Troebst, Conquest of the Sea 192–93 (1962) (English transl.).

lawyers were speculating and developing space law before the first Sputnik orbited; yet we merely whittle at the antiquated marine law when forced to by an item on the agenda of an international congress or a crisis. People who deal with the sea should sit down with distinguished lawyers with a view to a complete overhaul in the light of the imminent occupation and exploitation of the oceans.[9]

Finally, it is apparent that the increase in scientific investigation into the ocean both stimulates the need for developing legal prescriptions applicable to previously unknown types of interactions on the sea and provides technical information indispensable for creating new legal provisions. The Interagency Committee on Oceanography offers a succinct statement of this perspective:

> The "law of the sea" has historically been more conscientiously accepted as a code of international behavior than any other. Yet changes in prevailing rights of sovereignty, transit, and conservation increasingly depend on technological facts and scientific understanding. State as well as Federal legislators and policy makers must increasingly depend on oceanic science. When the interests of recreation, commercial fishing, sport fishing, oil exploration, and waste disposal compete for use of the same coastal resources, wise decisions that extend beyond preservation of the status quo can only be based on the fullest knowledge of the properties of the sea and its coastal areas. International disputes on defense aspects and fishing rights, which now occur with greater frequency, and matters of ownership of undersea mineral resources, sovereignty of straits or restricted waters or of strategically located sea mounts are a potential source of tension, and must be subject to agreements based on better data than now available.[10]

It is, thus, apparent that in spite of the considerable work lately devoted to clarification of, and agreement on, the law of the sea, persons closely associated with recent developments in ocean use, such as scientists and government officials, are disturbed about the capacity of the international legal system to deal with impending

[9] Spilhaus, *Man in the Sea*, 1st U.S. NAVY SYMPOSIUM ON MILITARY OCEANOGRAPHY ix–x (1964). And see statements of Dean Spilhaus, Dr. John C. Calhoun, Jr., and Representative Richard T. Hanna in *Hearings on S. 944 before the Senate Committee on Commerce*, 89th Cong., 1st Sess. (1965). See also Chapman, *Potential Resources of the Ocean, id.* at 132, 137.

[10] ICO, NATIONAL OCEANOGRAPHIC PROGRAM, FISCAL YEAR 1965, 2–3 (ICO Pamp. No. 15, March, 1964).

changes in exploitation of the ocean. Uneasiness exists about both the adequacy and availability of the legal tools that must be employed if grave and disruptive international controversy is to be avoided or minimized and about the level of attention devoted to emerging problems. It is not necessary to share fully the pessimism of some of these observers in order to find substance in their strictures about the lag in the evolution of legal prescriptions and structures appropriate to the needs of the new ventures upon the ancient resource that is the sea.[11]

It is not the purpose of this discussion to offer immediate remedies for the difficulties that can be anticipated. The objectives are rather to offer a preliminary, and necessarily brief, examination of the changes in the age-old process of interaction on the ocean that account in measure for the emergence of novel problems in regulation; to seek to identify some of the new problems by speculating about the types of future claims and counterclaims that will differ from those encountered in previous experience; and to make a short, rather general, survey of the broad outlines of the legal technicality inherited from the past that modern decision-makers might adopt, wisely or not, as useful for resolving disputes in the future. No systematic effort is made to clarify community policies at stake in the emerging struggle over the sea, though brief suggestions are made about the direction of further research on some problems.

[11] One point worth some emphasis in this connection is that scientists and engineers may not be the best source of legal advice about the sea. Despite the cogency of their admonitions about emergent legal problems, specific legal pronouncements from such sources should perhaps be scrutinized with care. To mention but one of several questionable instances that could be cited, one expert observer reports that "whale hunting is now rigidly controlled by international agreement." SPILHAUS, TURN TO THE SEA 29 (1959). This will come as something of a surprise to the International Whaling Commission which may yet come to be the model for ineffectual management of international resources. The commission has hardly rigidly controlled anything and the valuable blue whale is now almost nonexistent.

CHAPTER I

SIGNIFICANT FEATURES OF
PROCESS OF INTERACTION

A. PARTICIPANTS

In past centuries, states have played a familiar and important role in the exploration and utilization of the ocean and its resources; in view of trends in scientific inquiry and technological development, states' activity will probably be of even greater future significance. This expected state of affairs seems likely to eventuate no matter how a particular state arranges its internal social processes. For example, in the United States, where considerable emphasis is placed upon private initiative, it is amply clear that the federal government will occupy the dominant position in probing new ways and means of using the sea for national objectives.[12] Among the several, interdependent reasons for the special role of the state

[12] H. R. Rep. No. 2078, 86th Cong., 2d Sess. 25–29; ICO Pamp. No. 10, *supra* note 2, at 15–16. A representative of a private group, the National Association of Manufacturers, asserts that over half of "current expenditures" in the United States for ocean uses comes from private sources. Statement of John W. Clark on behalf of the NAM, in *Hearings concerning National Oceanographic Program Legislation before the Subcommittee on Oceanography of the House Committee on Merchant Marine and Fisheries,* 89th Cong., 1st Sess. 347 (1965). In any event, insofar as the oil industry is concerned, contribution to new ocean uses is likely to be incidental to technological developments directly useful to the industry. There is, of course, no reason to expect the oil industry to play a major role in disseminating hard-won, profitable scientific information.

15

are the relative paucity of knowledge of the ocean, the critical strategic character both of the oceanographic sciences and of the information sought in and of the oceans, the costly technology involved in the study and use of the sea and particularly of its more inaccessible parts, and that much of the projected activity in the sea does not immediately promise sufficient monetary gain to motivate consequential efforts by private groups. In combination, these factors suggest that comprehensive and sustained measures for developing new knowledge and uses of the sea require, and are likely to receive, an increasing level of support from the vast resources of the state, a level far above that available to, or reasonably expected from, private sources.[13] Available data disclose that the major industrial states of the world are greatly enlarging their commitment to oceanographic exploration and research.[14]

At the same time, it should occasion no surprise in view of the vastness of the ocean and the range of even its known resources that international governmental organizations are engaged in increasing intensity with exploratory work, partially in direct scientific inquiry, but mainly with co-ordination of numerous other activities in use of the sea.[15] The Intergovernmental Oceanographic Commission of UNESCO, among the newest of these organizations, is organizing numerous co-operative activities in the study of the sea.[16] Two recent and most ambitious of the projects operating through the IOC are the International Indian Ocean Expedition and the Tropical Atlantic Investigation. Other international organizations with wide-ranging interests that also are concerned with important aspects of oceanography include, in addition to UNESCO, the Food and Agriculture Organization, the Intergovernmental Maritime Consultative Organization, the International Atomic

[13] H. R. REP. No. 2078, 86th Cong., 2d Sess. 110–15.
[14] ICO Pamp. No. 10, *supra* note 2, at 39–41 offers appraisal of oceanographic efforts in the U.S.S.R., Japan, the United Kingdom, and Canada. Soviet work and facilities are examined in more detail in H. R. REP. No. 2078, 86th Cong., 2d Sess. 103–09. The increasing but still inadequate American involvement is partially chronicled in the annual projection of a National Oceanographic Program by the Interagency Committee on Oceanography.
[15] See generally the various numbers of INTERNATIONAL MARINE SCIENCE (Section h), the NEWSLETTER prepared by the UNESCO OFFICE OF OCEANOGRAPHY, and the BIOLOGY BRANCH of the FAO FISHERIES DIVISION for Reports on Activities; H. R. REP. No. 2078, 86th Cong., 2d Sess. 101–03; ICO, NATIONAL OCEANOGRAPHIC PROGRAM, FISCAL YEAR 1966, 34–37 (ICO Pamp. No. 17, Jan., 1965).
[16] INTERNATIONAL MARINE SCIENCE, *supra* note 15, Section d, reports on various international programs.

Energy Agency, the World Health Organization, and the World Meteorological Organization. Numerous regional and functional organizations might also be mentioned.[17]

Private associations, national and international, specializing in achieving a variety of goals have, for centuries, occupied a prominent position in ocean interactions. Groups devoted to production of wealth are most obvious, of course, though even the nature of these groups is altered as we discover new uses for ocean areas. For example, oil companies' investment in ocean-centered activities, including shipping and oil production, virtually unknown a few decades ago, now is the largest of any single private group. Among private international groups, those interested especially in enlightenment appear to have become unusually active recently, including the International Council of Scientific Unions, the Special Committee for Oceanic Research, the Special Committee for Antarctic Research, the International Geophysical Co-operation, 1959, the International Union of Biological Sciences, the International Union of Geodesy and Geophysics, and the Pacific Science Association.[18] Within particular states, there is also a very large number of private groups, such as universities and laboratories, active in study of the oceans.[19]

Private individuals are, in any case, the principal actors in interactions on the sea and have multiple interests in its use. In the field of science, the role of the individual acting wholly in his own behalf is reduced because of the reasons mentioned above, which are responsible for the increasing scope of state participation. Yet on a global basis the individual, without identification with other groups, is still a primary participant as he functions in a variety of roles including fisherman, sailor, swimmer, diver, researcher, businessman, and miner.

B. OBJECTIVES

Participants have for ages pursued all their values in and upon the sea, but the recent upsurge in interest in this area appears to

[17] See 1 *id.*, No. 3, Section b; 2 *id.*, No. 2, Section b.
[18] H. R. REP. No. 2078, 86th Cong., 2d Sess. 102–03.
[19] *Id.* at 58–70 lists U.S. institutions, including governmental.

17

be primarily concerned with increments in power, wealth, and enlightenment.

Everyone knows that states have continually resorted to the sea in many ways for promoting power objectives. Traditionally, the movement of ships, military and private, has been the chief form of exploiting the sea for power purposes, and states have engaged in frequent violent struggles to preserve or to acquire control over the ocean or strategic parts of it. And still today prominent observers emphasize that freedom of the seas includes, most importantly, the capacity to control the use of the sea by naval vessels.[20] But in the past decade or so, the opportunities for enhancement of power have involved methods of use greatly differing from the traditional, and these will undoubtedly undergo further changes as inquiry and exploration proceed. The major change, at least the one now discernible, arises from the advances in propulsion and in associated complex technology, which dramatically alter the conditions of access to the ocean.

Enlightenment is, in recent years, perhaps next only to power as the goal of participants, both public and private, in interactions on the sea. It has become a common activity for statesmen, politicians, and others to pronounce, with alarm, that knowledge of this vast domain is extremely limited and to forecast dire consequences if ignorance is not swept aside. Ever alert to sources of support, badly needed as it is, those who (in the United States at least) are aware of the shortage of knowledge and know-how relating to the sea and who are in a position to recommend appropriate action have energetically, and probably successfully, promoted substantial increases in government support of basic and applied oceanographic research. Scientists themselves have, as noted above, organized on an international scale, as the vastness and complexity of the subject demands, so that comprehensive and systematic achievement can be brought within reach.

The pursuit of wealth by exploiting the sea is ancient, and the traditional practices aimed at this object are familiar. But, as new opportunities are made available, the means for achieving wealth in the sea are being transformed. Within the past two decades, even within the last five years, wholly new industries and enterprises have

[20] See, e.g., *id.* at 12–13.

emerged for exploitation of the wealth potential of the ocean. Technological development permitting drilling on the ocean floor from platforms designed to be supported by the sea bed and, more importantly, from floating platforms is responsible for the spectacular spread of the oil industry to offshore areas of the United States, Saudi Arabia, Nigeria, Kuwait, and elsewhere.[21] The total investment in these ventures must be measured in the billions.[22] It seems certain that similar activity will be extended to areas beyond the geological continental shelf that are still shallow enough to permit economical operations. In addition, it is probably reasonable to speculate that sometime in the future, engineering techniques and facilities will be sufficiently developed to permit oil exploration and exploitation activities to be divorced completely from surface installations.

Other types of minerals are also present in great abundance in and under the oceans, including the deeper areas beyond the continental shelf. Estimates of the economic feasibility of exploiting the deeper ocean floor resources are not immediately promising, but the day is surely to come when these resources will be sufficiently scarce, and costs of the necessary technology reduced, to make ocean mining a viable enterprise for private groups.[23] Even before that time, of course, it is likely that governments will begin extraction of minerals from these inaccessible areas, perhaps to develop techniques useful for military purposes or to acquire prestige from the achievement.

C. SITUATIONS

The principal changes to be expected in the situational characteristics of ocean use pertain to the burgeoning expansion of interaction to parts of the sea beyond previous access and the beginnings of institutional practices in certain types of use of the ocean.

[21] A recent survey noted exploratory or exploitation activity in the above areas and in Canada, Mexico, Trinidad, Peru, Brazil, British Honduras, Guatemala, Surinam, the United Kingdom, Germany, Norway, Denmark, France, Spain, Italy, Ethiopia, Tunisia, Senegal, Pakistan, various Persian Gulf locations, Egypt, Gabon, Dhofar, U.S.S.R., Libya, Japan, Borneo, Australia, and Papua. 23 OFFSHORE No. 6, June 21, 1965 (ANNUAL MARINE DRILLING AND PRODUCING EDITION).

[22] Estimates of yearly expenditures for United States offshore exploitation are reported at $2 billion and for the world at $5 billion. 1 GEO-MARINE TECHNOLOGY No. 5, 22 (April, 1965).

[23] See *infra* pp. 31–33, and sources cited.

1. *Degree of Institutionalization in Use*

All participants in interactions concerning the sea have pursued their objectives in substantial independence of each other largely because the sea is so huge in relation to the technology of use that consequential interference with others is rather easily avoided. Even the largest-scale single use of the sea, now illustrated by hydrogen bomb–testing, which is by necessity exclusive of any other simultaneous use of the relatively immense area affected, could be and was carried out with very slight impact on other activities.[24] It may be doubted that this state of affairs will prevail much longer.

Beyond the need of co-operation for physical accommodation, the first area in which a considerable degree of organization in peaceful use has developed is, not unexpectedly, in scientific inquiry, the pattern of practices serving as the essential condition for development of wider uses of the ocean. Within a decade after World War II, recognition was general that to press effective attack on the formidable barriers of ignorance about the sea, it would be necessary to act in concert. Although this realization was not entirely novel (the International Council for the Exploration of the Sea was formed a half-century earlier), it was the first time for global efforts in co-ordination of individual national scientific projects and in active multilateral co-operation in specific projects. The initial framework of co-operation constructed for the International Geophysical Year is not being left entirely to wither, for since that great achievement, states have provided a permanent mechanism for governmental co-operation in the Inter-Governmental Oceanographic Commission. Numerous private groups, noted above, provide other structures for co-operation in activities aimed at the common goal of better understanding of the sea.

2. *Location of Interactions*

A major consequence of the expected discoveries about the ocean will be the expansion of human activities to vast areas of the earth hitherto even beyond any observation except the most indirect,

---

[24] See McDougal & Schlei, *The Hydrogen Bomb Tests in Perspective: Lawful Measures for Security,* 64 YALE L. J. 648, 682–84 (1955); but see Margolis, *The Hydrogen Bomb Experiments and International Law,* 64 *id.* at 629.

fleeting, and fragmentary. The increased sophistication of submarine vessel technology, the present potential and virtually certain future development of desirable resources in the deeper ocean areas beyond the shallow continental shelf, and the elaboration of the current tentative steps in developing underwater structures for human habitation will all contribute to the eventual spread of consequential interaction to previously accessible depths of the sea. A few brief comments about each of these factors seem worthwhile in anticipation of subsequent reference to legal controversies.

Formerly, of course, man was limited in direct access to the ocean to the surface and to submarine areas very near the surface, and, in the latter case, this access was temporally severely limited. During both world wars and for a considerable period after the second, the major moves of antagonists on the seas occurred either on the surface or only a relatively few fathoms below. For subsurface operations, vessels were, by the physical necessity of maintaining the necessary atmosphere, tied closely to the surface environment. Both these limitations upon access to the sea, restrictions on depths and time, are and have been undergoing major alterations. Now a most significant element of military force moves at depths greatly exceeding those previously considered possible for submarines. Moreover, these movements are, by virtue of new propulsion sources, divorced almost completely from the surface for very considerable periods.

This transformation in military craft is accompanied also by spectacular developments in other types of submersibles. Though not a real submarine, the underwater vehicle "Trieste" enables scientists to extend their range of direct observation to the deepest known parts of the ocean, at least for short periods.[25] In addition, other large submersible vehicles, which will permit access to depths of 15,000 feet, are now available or are under development, enabling direct exploration and observations of the sea and the bottom for over one-half its area. Smaller submersibles capable of operation at useful depths, down to several hundred feet, are also now engaged in significant exploration and investigation.

Still another development in technology permitting expansion of access to the sea is that of remote controlled vehicles utilizing external manipulators, which can be designed for a variety of par-

[25] H. R. REP. 2078, 86th Cong., 2d Sess. 79 ff.

ticular tasks in the deep sea. This technique of working on ocean tasks has been called a "telechiric" system, from Greek words for "distant hand."[26] A recent description of these systems indicates the potential in future use of this family of vehicles:

> Telechiric systems are considerably less familiar than divers and DSV's (deep submersible vehicles). However, enough experience with their practical operation has been obtained to demonstrate that they are feasible in an engineering sense and in a psychological sense. . . .
>
> The most significant point which has been gained by experience with telechiric systems is psychological. It was necessary to demonstrate by experiment that these systems can be learned, that no unusual operator skill is required, and that adequate speed and precision can be attained with a reasonable period of operator training.
>
> The principal advantages of the telechiric system derive from the separation of operator and vehicle. The operator is in a safe, normal environment; when necessary a group of experts can be assembled to work with the operator and advise him in some complex procedure. The telechiric vehicle can be designed to suit a particular group of tasks; it can be made large or small, fast or slow, versatile or simple, as required. There is no engineering limit to the working depth for which telechiric vehicles can be designed.
>
> The disadvantages of the telechiric system arise from its complexity. The telechiric vehicle must include a manipulating system; a sensory system; a command system; and a locomotor system. Even though it can be made small, it cannot be made extremely simple. Due primarily to the lack of experience with these vehicles they are quite costly and will remain so until the applications have developed to a point that will support a reasonable number of telechiric vehicles.
>
> Like the other manual techniques, telechiric vehicles are tool using vehicles. It is usually desirable to make the integral manipulators as simple as possible and to furnish the telechiric vehicle with a variety of tools adapted to particular tasks. These may be similar to the tools used by divers and by DSV's but adapted to the special needs of telechiric manipulators.[27]

[26] Clark, *Methods and Techniques for Sea-Floor Tasks,* 1 OCEAN SCIENCE AND ENGINEERING 1965, 267, 270 (1965). (Transactions of joint meeting of the Marine Technology Society and the American Society of Limnology and Oceanography, June 14–17, 1965, at Washington, D. C.)

[27] *Id.* at 271. See also Clark, *Application of Modern Remote Handling Techniques to Oceanography,* 1 MARINE SCIENCES INSTRUMENTATION 294 (1962) (A Collection of Papers Presented at the Marine Sciences Conference held Sept. 11–15, 1961, at Woods Hole, Mass.).

One kind of telechiric vehicle has been designed for operation directly on the ocean floor. Called the Remote Underwater Manipulator, it has been described as follows:

> It resembles a tank and is powered and controlled remotely by means of lightweight coaxial cable. Mobility is achieved on tracked wheel assemblies to which is affixed a mechanical arm similar in most respects to the type of manipulator used for remotely handling radioactive substances. The RUM vehicle can carry a payload of 1,000 pounds per square inch. It can maintain a speed of 2.6 knots and will travel to the limits of its five-mile-long cable. Its total weight—24,220 pounds. Guidance and control are accomplished from a shore-based operating station, and through the use of underwater television and illumination the operator will be able to view operations of the vehicle so as to make effective use of the prosthetic arm.[28]

Robot systems differ from the telechiric in that the latter are controlled from a distance, whereas the robot is designed to perform tasks without continued direction. Such devices are now in use by industrial enterprises at depths of 1,000 feet and below.

Lest it be mistakenly believed that science fiction is swiftly becoming reality only in the regions of outer space and not in the area of inner space, attention is due the recently expressed views of the former Oceanographer of the United States Navy, Rear Admiral E. C. Stephan:

> The future for development of manned and unmanned exploratory and instrumented undersea craft seems unlimited and will be dependent only on the speed with which manpower and resources are made available.[29]

Realism regarding resource potential requires that explicit distinction be made in terms of their location not only with respect to relationship to land masses but also, and particularly, in terms of depth of the area involved. The former distinction relates most significantly to problems of legal control, and the latter, more imme-

---

[28] H. R. REP. No. 2078, 86th Cong., 2d Sess. 136; and see Clark, in 1 MARINE SCIENCES INSTRUMENTATION, *supra* note 27, at 302–03.

[29] As quoted in interview with Murray Smith, 7 Data No. 4, 29 (April, 1962).

diately relevant for present purposes, concerns potentiality for exploration and, ultimately, exploitation. Insistence on the importance of depth is necessary as an antidote to undue optimism. It is, of course, widely known that numerous valuable minerals are now taken from the sea bed or subsoil or the water itself, but none of the present ocean mining efforts occurs in deeper water, i.e., in depths much below the continental shelf. The intense attention being devoted to deep sea mining by business enterprise suggests, however, that economic exploitation of this area may not be so far away as many believe.[30]

A final important condition affecting expansion of access involves the emplacement of structures, manned and unmanned, directly on the sea floor. This is one of the "emerging realities"[31] of oceanographic research and exploration, and it seems obvious that marked technological advance in developing underwater installations will have spectacular, if unforeseeable, effects upon the ways in which the sea is employed.[32] Perhaps a goodly portion of the relevant research is classified for military reasons and hence unavailable, but some information is in the public domain indicating the potentialities and problems involved.

The initial efforts are limited to relatively modest depths as would naturally be expected given the hostile character of the environment and the numerous problems of adapting human habitation to it. Even so, however, the depths in which experimenters are working are impressive. Thus, Jacques Cousteau and several associates remained thirty feet below the surface for one month, while others in his group dwelt for one week in a structure ninety feet down.[33] In June, 1964, Robert Stenuit and Jon Lindbergh remained for forty-nine hours at a depth of 430 feet in a structure designed by Edwin A. Link.[34] In July, 1964, United States Navy divers occupied an especially constructed undersea shelter, placed on the

---

[30] See *infra* pp. 31–33.

[31] The words are those in the quotation from H. R. Rep. No. 2078, *supra* note 7.

[32] One of the leading innovators in this field, Dr. Edwin Link, anticipates that within twenty years man "may live for days and weeks at the site of his labours" in the deep sea. See Link, *Working Deep in the Sea,* in 1 Calder ed., The World in 1984 103, 104 (Penguin Book, 1965).

[33] Dugan, Man under the Sea 402–03 (New, Rev. ed., Collier Books, 1965); Cousteau has discussed his earlier work in his book with James Dugan, The Living Sea (1964).

[34] See Groves, *Awake in the Deep,* 10 Sea Frontiers 285, 286–87 (1964).

sea floor at 192 feet in depth. The experiment was designed to last for three weeks; but bad weather required earlier termination, and the men had to come to the surface after eleven days. Despite the early ending, it is reported that the experiment was most productive, the most important result being the demonstration that divers could exist at such depth and for such a period without serious physiological harm. The same study offered this appraisal of future work:

> Incidentally, exploration of the abyss appears not *now* to be limited by the tremendous hydrostatic pressures encountered but rather by our present lack of knowledge of various human responses to the environment. For example, the phenomenon of inert gas narcosis (often called "Rapture of the Deep" when applied to nitrogen narcosis), is not yet understood in detail by underwater physiologists. The effect of inert gas narcosis can produce a virtual state of "drunkenness" when a diver is exposed for appreciable periods of breathing gas under high pressure. At present, helium is used, to a large extent, instead of nitrogen since it does not display any appreciable narcotic effect. However, possibly at some depth helium will cause narcosis.
>
> Still another potential limitation exists in the increased breathing resistance that takes place when a diver breathes gas under pressure. This is due to the increased density of the gas. The gas mixture used in SEALAB-I increased the breathing resistance to approximately 1.6 times that of air at the surface. This effect causes some degree of lung fatigue which should increase with increasing depth.
>
> In spite of the known and unknown obstacles in the way, many problem areas are soon to benefit from the recent SEALAB effort. Among these are those of salvage, submarine rescue, underwater construction, underwater inspection and repair (cables, pipelines, etc.), strategic applications (ASW warning installations, coastal defenses, submarine bunkering stations) ocean floor mining, fish and underwater crop farming and oil drilling.[35]

Operation Sealab II took place during the summer of 1965. In this more ambitious experiment, or cluster of experiments, the Sealab was placed a depth of 205 feet off the coast of La Jolla, California, and was occupied by succeeding teams of aquanauts for a total stay

[35] *Id.* at 294. Copyright 1964 by SEA FRONTIERS, published by the International Oceanographic Foundation, Miami, Florida.

of forty-five days. One aquanaut, Commander Scott Carpenter, occupied Sealab for the first thirty-day period.[36]

D. BASE VALUES

Power, wealth, enlightenment, and skill appear certain to be most potent among the many values (or assets) that states and other participants will employ in attaining their goals in the ocean. It is traditional to note the special importance of the ocean in the aggregate power position of some states. In very recent times, in the last decade, the historic role of the sea as a power base may be seen to have altered greatly; for with the completely new weapons systems created by both the United States and the Soviet Union (i.e., the Polaris-type nuclear submarine, carrying nuclear missiles), the sea now serves as the location for a powerful offensive weapons system capable of reaching into the interior of major land masses, and it is no longer significant only as a medium for transport of troops and goods vital to war efforts. These new submarine-missile systems have for their major, most highly valued characteristic that of great mobility and concealment. The attribute of concealment has thus far, in the opinion of many, offered mutual advantage to the major opponents since, by permitting each side to possess an invulnerable deterrent to comprehensive nuclear attack, it has stabilized an extremely dangerous military confrontation.

It merits special emphasis that one critical effect of expanded oceanographic research may be to disturb the stability hitherto associated with submarine missile-launching systems. At the present level of knowledge, the ocean is regarded as largely opaque—only the transmission of sound permits the detection of submerged vehicles and objects, and, thus far, such detection is reliable only within limited distances.[37] Should long-range detection devices emerge as a result of expanded research efforts, the consequences

[36] Reports on this latest experiment are not available at this writing, but it has been announced that Sealab II will be the subject of a symposium to be held in January, 1966. 3 MARINE TECHNOLOGY SOCIETY MEMO, No. 2, p. 1, September, 1965.

[37] H. R. REP. No. 2078, 86th Cong., 2d Sess. 17. In September, 1965, it was reported that since 1963–64 the United States has been operating an underwater detection system effective for submarines approaching to within a few hundred miles of the Atlantic Coast. N.Y. Times, September 14, 1965, p. 3, col. 1.

could be dangerous, though, to be sure, the significance of this development, when and if it comes, depends upon the total military-politico-scientific context in which it occurs. At present, the known acquisition of this detection capacity by one of the cold war antagonists might have a deeply disturbing impact on expectations concerning the use of violence. Perhaps it is not too far-fetched to imagine that successful achievement in long-distance detection by one cold war antagonist might deliberately be shared with the other, lest the ensuing instability in the power structure lead to costly adventures by one or another of the opponents.

It is to be expected, when one views wealth as a base value, that those with high positions with respect to this value are favored in achieving access to the expanding oceanic environment; and those already relatively well off in this respect are, not unexpectedly, more likely to gain in wealth position than are others. This feature, certainly not unique to this particular process of interaction, may, of course, lead to initiatives by those in a less favorable wealth position to subject some ocean resources to organized inclusive use, thus hopefully providing for augmentation in the basic wealth position of states generally, rather than just of a relative few. The prospects of success for such proposals are not sanguine, but the degree of success attending them will depend upon numerous factors in the future context. We know, of course, that the major resources of the continental shelf were allocated according to territorial notions, with each coastal state receiving exclusive rights of use, and that no serious attention was ever given to the thought of providing for organized international control of, and benefit from, the area.[38]

Enlightenment promises to be a more significant base value in the future than it has in the past, perhaps more than any other value. The scientific study of the sea is a relatively new enterprise, and because of this, in part, no participant has any outstandingly advantageous position as yet. Nonetheless, only a relatively few states, and very few private groups, possess much knowledge of the sea, its processes, and its resources. For the vast majority of states in the world, the ocean is a body of water over which ships can move and from which fish can be hunted and taken, and it is no more than that. Among a handful of states, the scientific investiga-

[38] See McDougal & Burke, The Public Order of the Oceans 631–42 (1962).

tion of the sea has, on the other hand, a longer history; and for two, the Soviet Union and the United States, the pursuit of such inquiry is a strategic enterprise the neglect of which could impose drastic disadvantages in power position. If understanding of the complexities of the ocean environment continues to be a critical component of the total strategy, it seems probable that the benefits, actual and potential, of new information about the ocean will be limited severely. The result may be to foreclose or greatly hamper the employment of presently available resources by states generally, as well as the acquisition and enjoyment of new base values.

Availability of reservoirs of special skills pertaining to the sea is a traditional asset in making use of the area; and as the world looks with increasing attention to the ocean, this value becomes correspondingly magnified in importance. An enormous range of skills is, of course, relevant in connection with such complex phenomena as the ocean, including those in a great many areas of the natural and physical sciences, engineering, communications, navigation, and propulsion. The state or other participant that may command or enlist such a varied group of skills as these and others is enabled to seek and attain a substantial increment in its total value position and is able, further, to enlarge the store of assets upon which it may draw in employing the ocean and its resources. Unfortunately for the community as a whole, the distribution of skills does not appear to be adjusted to the need for drawing upon ocean resources. For example, the areas having the greatest need for new sources of food are the same areas that suffer most from a lack of some of the skill groups that could contribute significantly to meeting the need.

E. STRATEGIES

All available strategies will continue to be employed by all participants as the future of the ocean for mankind unfolds, but certain changes are reasonably foreseeable in the way certain of the policy instruments are wielded. In terms of the management of goods and services, observers and policy-makers continue to emphasize reliance on the sea as an important source of food for the millions of deprived around the world.[39] There are widely known difficulties in increasing the agricultural productivity of land in adequate measure to provide for swiftly increasing populations. At the same time we know that fish from the sea furnish a significant part of the diet for peoples in a number of countries around the world and, perhaps more importantly, that animal protein from the sea is very useful as food for land animals that are more highly desirable forms of food than fish. So useful is fishmeal for chicken feed that Wilbert Chapman has observed that "it is chickens, rather than humans directly, that are stimulating the important part of the increase in the world fish production."[40] And it is also thought that the fish productivity of the sea is now relatively untapped.[41] In these circumstances it would be surprising if there were *not* optimistic statements about the desirability and possibility of more intensive efforts to utilize ocean fisheries.

For present purposes, the realism of the more optimistic estimates of the provender present and within reach in the sea need not be appraised, though the difficulty of the task of exploiting these resources in helpful ways is probably grossly misperceived by many,[42] for it is likely that some substantial increase in food productivity can be achieved. And no matter how great the increase may or can actually be, planners and policy-makers in needy states and communities will probably proceed on the assumption that a larger proportion of investment resources ought to be allocated to this sector of the total economy. The extent to which these planning decisions are made and effectuated and the degree of success achieved may depend, in large measure, on the continued study of the ocean in all its aspects, including, but not limited to, the role of the marine biologist and ecologist. It may be added separately, for appropriate emphasis, that national planning in the direction of increasing man's dependence on the sea also requires inquiry into

[39] ICO Pamp. No. 10, *supra* note 2 at 10–11; Spilhaus, *Oceanography: A Wet and Wondrous Journey*, 20 BULL. ATOM. SCIENTISTS 11 (Dec., 1964); STEWART, THE GLOBAL SEA 98 (Van Nostrand Searchlight Book, 1963).

[40] Chapman, *Potential Resources of the Ocean*, in *Hearings on S. 944 before the Senate Committee on Commerce*, 89th Cong., 1st Sess., 132 (1965). This is an excellent summary of knowledge in this general area and it is exceptionally informative and notably provocative in the discussion of fisheries resources.

[41] *Id.* at 143–52.

[42] Letter from Giulio Pontecorvo, 21 BULL. ATOM. SCIENTISTS No. 5, pp. 33–34 (May, 1965); Christy, *Efficiency in the Use of Marine Resources* (RESOURCES FOR THE FUTURE, Reprint No. 49) (Sept., 1964).

the social sciences, including all of the complex factors affecting our varying perspectives about the ocean.

Among the sociological factors perhaps worth inquiry are the various cultural characteristics that may influence perceptions about the ocean and its resources. Religious beliefs, for example, may be important for their impact upon the nature and scope of fishing operations by certain groups.[43] Considerations of status in the community are known to have affected willingness to venture out into the farther reaches of the sea.[44] Summary indication of potential research in this area is contained in the following excerpt from a report of an imaginary conference held to consider the relationship of man and the sea:

> The Panel on Marine Agriculture suggested that several research tasks in comparative analysis of maritime communities might shed light on the problem of "cultivating the cultivators." One recommended study was analysis of ethnological data (beginning with the Human Relations Area Files) to determine the critical variables accounting for differences and anomalies in cultural attitudes toward fishing and fish consumption. (Related to this, the Committee on Marine Concepts was charged with gathering and classifying the concepts involved in acquiring and utilizing all forms of marine life as food in various languages, cultures and subcultures.) Numerous maritime societies and cultures have had what appears to be the same economic need and physical opportunity to use marine food resources. Some have developed the attitudes, skills and social structure to permit at least partial exploitation of these resources; others have not. Analysis of such contrasts, it was felt, might provide a more solid foundation for creating the requisite skills and conditions among various populations.
>
> Attention was directed to important cultural variations not only in the technology of fishing, and the degree of exploitation of marine resources, but also in the social functions of these activities. Comparative study of fishing and fish consumption from the perspective of cultural dynamics might lead to understanding the kinds of obstacles that exist, even in modernizing maritime cultures, to a rational exploitation of oceanic food resources.
>
> Central to this kind of research would be a study of social change as it relates to fishing and fish consumption. Several historians were invited to begin scrutiny of available data to determine the social factors at work in the waxing and waning of fishing and fish con-

[43] MORGAN, WORLD SEA FISHERIES 86 (1956).
[44] *Id.* at 175.

sumption in various eras and civilizations. Studies of fishing communities and of fishermen, it was noted, had pointed to a sort of "fishing weltanschauung"; the fisherman has often seemed embedded less in an economic or occupational pursuit than in a way of life. In the traditional fishing community, requisite skills and attitudes are transmitted almost as esoteric lore from generation to generation, and observers have often remarked the tenacity with which fishing communities resist forces that might change their pattern of life. (They hold this tenacity in common with sailors; both groups tend to ignore or resist either marked deprivation or reward as incentives for occupational change.) This raised questions relating to the necessary and sufficient conditions for introducing modern technology into the world's fishing industries on the required scale. Would enough change-minded individuals emerge among traditional fishing and diving groups to carry out the transformation? Or would a virtually new class of marine workers be required? If so, how would they be recruited and from what population groups?[45]

Part of the point of calling attention to this proposal here is that, if it should be acted upon and deliberate manipulative techniques are employed to create and to stimulate increased use of ocean resources, it might be possible, or imperative, to anticipate the emergence of controversy regarding access to particular resources and to avoid serious strife.

Turning from cultural to material considerations, one finds that the more specific techniques for increasing the oceanic contribution to world food resources embrace refinements and imaginative developments in detection and location of fish, harvesting methods, environmental modifications, communications, materials, propulsion, and processing.[46] The new procedures, already under development or envisaged as technologically feasible, profit from research into military and space problems and seek to adapt to the above-mentioned phases of fishery exploitation such diverse modalities as radar, infra-red procedures, laser beams, underwater acoustics, artificial methods of fish aggregation (including electrical, optical, olfactory, chemical, air bubbles, and remotely controlled self-pro-

[45] Cameron, *Ahoy, Marine Sociology,* 4 THE AMER. BEHAV. SCIENTIST 3, 4–5 (No. 7, Mar., 1961).
[46] See Alverson & Wilimousky, *Prospective Developments in the Harvesting of Marine Fishes,* 2 MODERN FISHING GEAR OF THE WORLD 583–88 (1964) (From paper presented at 2d FAO World Fishing Gear Congress, 1963).

31

pelled gear and underwater vehicles), fish farming and fertilizing, satellite communication (including television), improved navigation systems, materials technology, engine and ship design, nuclear radiation, refrigeration, and, finally, but by no means least, computer technology. An imaginative projection of future world fishing methods has been offered by American and Canadian fisheries experts, who regard the eventual occurrence of these anticipated changes as "undebatable":

A fictional picture of fishing in the future might run along the following lines:

A net of unmanned buoys has been established for several years in the sea and the patterns of occurrence and distribution of natural resources have been determined and plotted. The buoys are interrogated at regular intervals through satellite telemetering and from their surface transmitters by pulse-coded sonic means to instrument heads at various depths in the sea. Transmission redundancy is reduced to a minimum as only points of parameter change are telemetered. As the data come in to "hydro-central" . . . computers reduce the mass of informational bits to contoured plots of biological oceanographic and meteorological parameters. By facsimile techniques, these data summaries are transmitted to the research laboratory and fishing centres of the world. When a biological parameter anomaly occurs, the nearest buoy would automatically be instructed to assess the nature of the instance with high-resolution sonar and autospectrophotometric methods. These data would be transmitted back to hydro-central for computer and human interpretation. The movements of the identified resources would be plotted.

In some instances it might be necessary to verify the nature of the resource or an anomaly by an on-the-spot check using aircraft perhaps equipped with Laserscopes or hydro-foil research craft equipped with high-speed self-propelled submersible television vehicles. Depending on the species, the main fishing fleet could be deployed into the path of the fish, or conversely, suitable deterrents could be placed in the sea to guide the fish to the catcher. Aircraft could disperse the necessary chemical pellets to olfactorily guide the fish, or remote-controlled underwater vehicles would produce the necessary electrical-sonic or bubble barrier to perform the same function. Depending on the depth of harvest, catches would be performed by catcher boats assigned to permanently anchored factory ships or by automated underwater vehicles operated from ship or shore stations.

Surveillance of the main plotting board in hydro-central would allow detection of weather conditions and precursors of El Nino type shifts in advance. Similarly, areas of high or low basic nutrient production could be watched and, with broad environmental limits, spawning populations deflected accordingly.[47]

That the ocean has always had a profound impact on military strategies hardly needs prolonged examination or explanation. Recently, the dimensions of military operations at sea have undergone considerable change, for submarine missile systems are now a major, perhaps the chief, component of military power. In this sense, the ocean today clearly has greater relative importance for the world than it has had in all human history. It is certain that ocean-based weapons systems have never played so critical a role, for now such systems are employed, or may be employed, either for threatening global destruction or for preserving the world from indescribable devastation. The suddenness of this awesome addition to the strategic nature of the sea illustrates what can happen in this area as a result of scientific developments, perhaps initially unrelated to the ocean, and suggests the wisdom of anticipating future changes in the military instrument of policy as a result of the new emphasis on ocean sciences.

From the perspective of all available strategies open to participants, it has long been apparent that in time of "peace" the principal mode of operation has been non-competitive and that each participant could in very substantial degree engage in its own strategies irrespective of those employed by others. It definitely seems possible that this state of affairs is to terminate in the not-too-distant future. The reason for this is simply that the conditions of use of the sea may undergo such change that explicit co-ordination of strategies becomes necessary. In respect to the exploitation of resources, for example, it seems more than likely that it will be necessary to join in co-operative activity, utilizing the resources of a variety of participants and excluding or limiting the competing activities of others.[48] In the case of fisheries, for specific illustration, the necessary condition for increasing productivity may be the initiation of joint efforts in estimating the size, location, and temporal duration of certain stocks; in determining the amount of effort that

[47] Alverson & Wilimousky, *supra* note 46, at 588–89; see also Hardy, *New and Richer Marine Harvests Forecast,* 1 CALDER, *op. cit. supra* note 32, at 100–03, for reference to use of "tractor-trawls" for fishing.

[48] Crutchfield & Pontecorvo, *Crisis in the Fisheries,* 18 BULL. ATOM. SCIENTISTS No. 9, pp. 18–20 (Nov., 1962); Christy, *supra* note 42.

should be devoted to particular stocks; and in providing for the ways in which the yield can be limited and shared. Without joint decisions such as this on matters affecting access and use, the benefits of an enlarged potential gain may be frittered away.

This same possible need for explicit co-ordination of strategy may also, someday, be accepted in manipulating military instruments. There is already, as noted below, explicit mention of joint strategies on employment of submarines.[49]

F. OUTCOMES

The question here is what effect the new interest in the sea, evidenced by intensified scientific and technological research therein, may have upon the shaping and sharing of values from interactions on the ocean. That value production will increase seems certain, as even the brief discussion below suggests, but it seems also likely that the distribution of values among participants may, for the short run at least, become more restricted. The process is likely to be a selective one, with some values becoming more widely held and others relatively less so.

1. *Power*

Historically, it is evident that the ocean served to enhance the power of some states far more than others, even though the technology and skills necessary for access to the sea seem primitive by modern standards and hence rather generally available. It will be no great change, therefore, if increments in power resulting from new forms of employing the sea accrue to very few participant states. It seems amply clear that some of the new methods for achieving access to, and control of, the sea will not be widely available, at least in the first years of this modern effort at conquering the sea. The emerging discoveries in many scientific areas relating to access to the ocean will be too heavily imbued with military applications and connotations for their general dissemination. Moreover, the new technology of the sea promises to be both costly and much more difficult to develop than the vehicles and instruments custom-

[49] See text *infra* at note 65.

arily employed in traversing the sea. The development of deep-sea vehicles and structures, in most obvious illustration, appears to be an expensive and complex undertaking, and its results may not be widely shared for decades.[50]

2. Wealth

The potentialities in greater productivity of wealth are probably beyond realistic measurement at this time. Outcomes that have significance for wealth include increased fishery production, production of gas and oil, the discovery and exploitation of other minerals, improvements in surface navigation systems, development of submarine navigation, utilization of the sea as a source of power, improvements in meteorology, and possible capacity to modify climate and weather.[51]

Even with current technology, some estimate that fishery yield can be expanded five times over without danger to continued productivity, and one expert has declared that "If this renewable source of food is harvested properly, we might steadily take from five to perhaps a hundred times the present amount out of the sea."[52] As mentioned above in brief summary, improvements in gear, more efficient designs in fishing vessels, better underwater sound detection, sophisticated techniques for detection of commercial quantities of fish, and more adequate management policies and procedures can be expected to lead to high levels of productivity. All this

[50] It is reported, however, that "there are at least two dozen companies in the Free World producing non-military dry submarines." Hull, *World Ocean Market Report,* 1 GEO-MARINE TECHNOLOGY 7, 23 (No. 5, April, 1965). Nonetheless the larger deep submersibles come high, the "Auguste Piccard" costing $1.5 million to build in Switzerland. And Hull reports that "The 1,000 foot, two-man Cousteau-Westinghouse diving saucer "Soucoup" and its support ship and crew, for example, leases to Scripps Institution of Oceanography for $70,000 per month plus an extra charge for each dive." *Ibid.* See also Clark, *supra* note 26, at 271.

[51] For analysis of benefits for the United States alone see NAS-NRC, ECONOMIC BENEFITS FROM OCEANOGRAPHIC RESEARCH (Publ. No. 1228, 1964). Excluding some very productive resources, such as petroleum, this report declared: "Our estimates indicate that a continuing national investment in oceanography of approximately $165 million a year (not counting the part for national defense) will be an essential component in bringing about savings of nearly three billion dollars a year, plus added annual production worth almost as much. Ten to 15 years will be needed to achieve these gains, and other expenditures in addition to those for marine research will be required if they are to be realized" (*Id.* at 1–2). See also NATIONAL SECURITY INDUSTRIAL ASSOCIATION, A NATIONAL OCEAN PROGRAM 9–48 (1964).

[52] Spilhaus, *supra* note 39, at 12.

activity aimed at improvement in yield must also be accompanied, it deserves emphasis, by efforts to stimulate demand for, and consumption of, fish and by resort to methods for encouraging allocation of labor and resources to this form of enterprise. Moreover, if the increment in wealth from the sea is to be distributed properly, all these factors affecting increased fishery yield must be brought to the attention of, or made available to, policy-makers in the lesser developed states of the world.

Mineral resources of the ocean are most commonly thought about whenever attention is turned to wealth production from the sea. The high promise of this aspect of ocean use has already, of course, been realized in part since important and lucrative oil production now may be found off the coasts of a growing number of countries. Very recently the search for oil and gas has been extended to the North Sea, where a find of commercial quantities would be significant, perhaps as much in terms of political transformation as in dollars and cents. Some notion of the possibilities of this area is to be seen both in the large number of companies involved in the North Sea search and in the heavy expenditures, several hundred million dollars, that will be disbursed for exploration in the next several years.[53]

With respect to other minerals one authoritative source has summarized the situation as follows:

> Diamonds are recovered along the coast of South Africa, tin is dredged from shallow waters off the Indonesian Archipelago, Japan mines iron from its coastal waters, and heavy minerals are taken from beaches and near beach areas of the United States, Australia and India. Sulfur is recovered from beneath the Gulf of Mexico. Coal has been mined from tunnels extending from land to points under the sea in Canada and England, and bromine, magnesium, iodine and common salt are recovered commercially from sea water.
> However, all present marine mining is in relatively shallow waters less than 400 feet in depth, and the equipment employed is generally the conventional hydraulic or bucket dredge. Normal evaporation, chemical precipitation, and ion-exchange procedures are applied to the removal of compounds and elements from salt water. Thus, there is no true deep-sea mining industry today.

[53] See generally 23 OFFSHORE No. 6, June 21, 1965 (Annual Marine Drilling and Producing Edition).

The major deterrent to further extension of even the shallow-water mining, to say nothing of deep-sea mining, is cost. But there is also lack of a clear picture of where and what the resources are. The problems of investigation are formidable. At present, the industry lacks efficient methods and equipment either for prospecting or mining the sea bottom, it lacks knowledgeable marine scientists and engineers, and it lacks incentive since present sources are adequate to satisfy present markets.

It has heard the reports of manganese, phosphorus, gold, platinum, tin, and a host of other minerals found on the continental shelf or the deep sea floor; but looking at the cost-benefit relationships, the mining industry is apparently obliged to wait until there has been a large-scale, long-range comprehensive program of exploration before venturing very far into this difficult region. In the national interest, the initial exploration may be the role of government.[54]

The difficulties emphasized by this report may be somewhat less than overwhelming, and perhaps its cautious tone should be viewed with some skepticism. It is not, however, necessarily inconsistent with this caution to find it reported within two years of issuance of this statement that "An American shipbuilding company is financing the first commercial attempt to mine the manganese nodules scattered over wide areas of the Pacific bottom."[55] And shortly thereafter it was announced that the United States Bureau of Mines, in collaboration with two commercial enterprises, was undertaking an underwater mining research venture.[56]

Perhaps reports about these ventures stimulated the declaration from a Soviet source that "Available data indicate that the USA has already begun to exploit these truly untouched reserves."[57] In

[54] ICO Pamp. No. 10, *supra* note 2, at 20–21.

[55] N.Y. Times, Jan. 30, 1965, p. 41, col. 3.

[56] Private concerns have been working in this new activity for some time. The President of Alpine Geophysical Associates, Inc., has written that ". . . since 1959 Alpine has conducted a number of ocean mining exploration programs and has outfitted and operated the requisite 'Ocean Mining Research Vessels.' These programs have included surveys for tin offshore Thailand, coal offshore England, Scotland, Wales, Japan, and Australia, iron ore offshore Japan and Canada, undisclosable natural resources offshore New York, New Jersey and Florida, and diamonds offshore South Africa (1 GEO-MARINE TECHNOLOGY No. 6, p. 39 [May–June, 1965]).

[57] Kaplin, *Underwater Geology*, Series XII: GEOLOGY AND GEOGRAPHY (All-Union Society for the Dissemination of Political and Scientific Information, Moscow, 1963) (Excerpts transl. by Jt. Publ. Res. Svc., June 27, 1963) (J.P.R.S. 19, 908).

this same Soviet study, reserves of raw manganese on the floor of the Pacific Ocean alone were estimated at ninety trillion tons.

Surface transport over the sea has long benefited from oceanographic research; hence, further contributions are merely a continuation of previous trends. The forms of the new assistance from science are, however, likely to appear greatly exotic to many, such as provision for more precision in navigation by use of space satellites, the aid of satellites in regular communication, and the selection of more economical routes as a result both of better understanding of the physical movements in the sea and of more adequate weather predictions.[58]

Subsurface transportation may offer great potentialities for wealth production since such a mode of travel would permit year-round use of ice-bound waters and hence afford much shorter routes between major centers.[59] In addition, and no less important, movement below the ocean surface does not have to contend with the vagaries of weather or even the normal operation of wind and wave. The emergence of subsurface transport systems will also bring with it requirements for facilities and equipment not now devised or, perhaps, even conceived.

Another potentially large contribution to wealth might be forthcoming from the effect of better knowledge of the ocean upon meteorology. There is an intimate relationship between the ocean and the atmosphere; therefore, scientific study of the one is useful also for the understanding of the other. The benefits to be gained may be enormous if the new knowledge being generated can be employed to protect man from the tremendous losses inflicted annually as a result of the violent storms born in the ocean. Beyond this protection against large-scale catastrophe, there are many more or less mundane benefits that might be within reach, such as prevention of erosion and of tidal and wave damage.[60]

The control of climate and weather is easily seen to have a great impact upon wealth positions, among others; and in a project for this climate control, knowledge of the ocean would be a critical factor. A report of the House Committee on Science and Astronautics declares:

[58] NAS-NRC, *supra* note 51, at 28–36.
[59] ICO Pamp. No. 10, *supra* note 2, at 22; Link, *supra* note 32, at 105; H. R. Rep. 2078, 86th Cong., 2d Sess. 52.
[60] See generally NAS-NRC, *supra* note 51, 36–39.

Eventually, man desires to control climate, to enjoy the salubrious effect of mild and predictable weather. It would seem that the sheer mass of this natural phenomenon would defy adjustment. On the other hand scientists are confronted with many processes in which a condition exists of incipient instability. Like sitting on a fence, only relatively small forces or investments of energy are necessary to cause the process to swing radically from one side to another.

If these processes could be controlled, the impact for constructive purposes by their application to marginal lands, thus to feed an increasing population of the future, will be significant. The military use of climate control carries with it more sinister implications. The nation that could influence the rainfall of another might well control the destiny of the world.[61]

3. *Enlightenment*

It is, perhaps, testimony of the long history of disregard for comprehensive efforts at scientific study of the oceans that the outcome most likely to be promoted in highest degree as a result of the recent intensification of interest in the ocean is the enhancement of knowledge. In part, the additions to knowledge may appear great because the fund now on hand is so relatively slight. Yet, in another more vital sense, the increment in enlightenment will loom large because much of what is to be discovered is of fundamental importance for so many areas of human interaction. Thus the significance of scientific inquiry into the sea in all its many phases relates, *inter alia*, to discoveries about the origins of the planet and the life inhabiting it, about the origin and location of the major continents, about the origins of the oceans themselves as the largest physical feature of our planet, about the relationship between this planet (as well as of certain particular features of it) and other planets in our universe, and about the composition of and processes occurring in the planet. These matters touch upon and may illuminate questions that have perplexed mankind for centuries. Numerous, more specific discoveries, of course, remain to be made—the import of which cannot now be anticipated.

61 H. R. REP. 2078, 86th Cong., 2d Sess. 52.

CHAPTER   II

PROCESS OF CLAIM

By far the most significant changes to be anticipated among the salient features of the process of claim are in the types of claims that are likely to be advanced as controversies arise concerning the exploration and enjoyment of ocean areas and resources.

In previous inquiry into the law of the sea in collaboration with Professor Myres S. McDougal, it was found convenient to employ a structure of claim and counterclaim designed to call attention to the concentrations of inclusive and exclusive interests in the ocean and to aid in the identification of special interests.[62] One consequence of this method of inquiry was to focus attention more upon geographical areas than upon functional uses of the sea. In the following section, the system of organization adopted is one that seeks to place greater emphasis upon the kinds of uses and competences that could become the subject of controversy.[63]

---

[62] McDougal & Burke, op. cit. supra note 38, at 29.

[63] The structure of claim projected for the purposes of this paper is not completely comprehensive. It is realized, for example, that the section on resources is focused rather narrowly and that the claims to competence to prescribe and apply policy could be expanded. We have also omitted, intentionally, any consideration of claims associated uniquely with periods of active violence or very high expectations of violence.

A. CLAIMS RELATING TO ACCESS

1. *Claims to Inclusive and Exclusive Access*

Traditionally, states have sought to protect the movement of the manned vehicles that, for many different purposes, they have sent out upon, over, and under the oceans. Future conflicting claims to access may arise in connection with the movement, or emplacement, of novel types of manned and unmanned vehicles and objects. Such types include the telechiric systems (operating either as a bottom-crawler or through the water as a "conventional" submersible), the robot systems, the various inhabited submersibles capable of operating at continental shelf depths and deeper, the special structures developed for prolonged habitation in submerged regions, and the various types of buoy systems that are unmanned but either inert in the water or self-propelled.

Among the manned vehicles, the eventual employment of telechiric systems, including bottom crawlers, for exploration and exploitation may lead to controversy over rights of access. The principal claim here will probably center about the traditional doctrine of freedom of the seas in the effort to secure free access for these vehicles to all areas of the sea floor outside the territory of a particular state. And within state territory, demands for uninhibited movement may still be advanced as these vehicles have occasion to enter the submarine areas of another state. Differences about rights of access, if any arise, are likely to be sharpest in connection with the use of the state territory within the limits of the territorial sea. Coastal states may contend, for example, that coastal auhority over access is not limited by the doctrine of innocent passage and that the coastal state may therefore completely exclude such vehicles from passing on or over the ocean floor within the territorial sea. And even if a state were to concede that the community of states should be permitted to have some access, under a right of innocent passage, it might claim a greater scope of authority to qualify telechiric systems, including bottom-crawlers, as offensive to particular coastal interests than was, or would be, claimed with respect to conventional surface vessels.

Beyond the territorial sea, but within the adjacent area of the continental shelf, coastal states might seek to deny access to telechiric vehicles employed for exploration or exploitation. Since the floor underlying the oceanic part of the planet was not, until recent years, open to direct access by man, there is an understandable lack of customary or conventional international-law prescriptions upon which to base claims to exclusive control over access to interactions there. Beyond the territorial sea, at least, the only use of the ocean floor, as a spatial extension resource, was for the purpose of laying cables to establish communications between the continents and islands, and it was universally agreed that access to this area for this purpose was inclusive. This meant that each state had authority to engage in cable-laying and that no state could exclude any other from engaging in this activity. But with the development of a technology permitting drilling for oil in areas beyond the territorial sea, states did claim an exclusive competence over the sea bed and subsoil for this purpose. So widely were these claims pressed that international agreement was rather quickly obtained making it explicit that each state has "sovereignty" over the continental shelf for purposes of exploring and exploiting its mineral and certain animal resources. This agreement, the Continental Shelf Convention of 1958, also sought to provide for accommodation of the authority of coastal states for this purpose with other actual and potential activities in this area, including those undertaken for cable communication and scientific investigation.[64]

But the existence of the Continental Shelf Convention, with its provisions seeking to accommodate exclusive access for limited purposes with inclusive access for others, does not necessarily preclude conflicting claims to access, as new techniques in exploration and use of the sea emerge and become refined. Thus it seems possible, though how likely cannot be determined, that coastal states may seek to exclude access by bottom-crawlers, for example, to engage in certain types of activities, including scientific, either completely or on condition that detailed accounts of the locations and projected work are furnished the coastal state in advance. The convention already contains certain limitations on access for oceanographic investigations; but as new techniques are developed, states might claim to extend the scope of their exclusive controls.

When bottom-crawlers and other remotely controlled vehicles become available for military purposes, if such operation proves

---

[64] 2 OFFICIAL RECORDS, *op. cit. supra* note 1, at 142–43; see generally McDOUGAL & BURKE, *op. cit. supra* note 38, at 691–724.

useful, the possibility of conflicting claims over access by this type of vehicle may be heightened. One reason for this is that such vehicles could, on occasion, inspire grave apprehensions of threat to adjacent land and sea areas. In conjunction with the development of deep submersibles, the operation of bottom-crawlers may add new dimensions to the range of undesirable impacts of operations at sea upon coastal interests. Indeed, the possible uses of surface vessels, perhaps considered inimical to the interests of adjacent states, may be expanded by the co-ordinated operations of inhabited submersibles and telechiric systems, including bottom-crawlers, not to speak of aircraft, missiles, and satellites. The result may be that states adjacent to an area of such use might claim to exclude all of the associated equipment, including the submarine devices, from the region involved. Support might be sought in asserted authority over contiguous zones for security or over the use of the continental shelf for military purposes. Counterclaims asserting free access may be expected to emphasize, not surprisingly, the traditional doctrine of freedom of the seas, contending that inclusive access to ocean areas, historically protected through invocation of this principle, extends to protect not only craft moving through the water or on the surface but also vehicles on the bottom or positioned there.

As the employment of remotely controlled vehicles, including bottom-crawlers, becomes more commonplace, the demands for exclusive control by one state may arise also from inconsistent uses of the submarine regions, in addition to demands stemming from anticipated detrimental impact on land-based interactions. Presently, for illustration, some states use limited areas of the ocean bottom for the storage of low-level radioactive waste materials. Although these areas are very limited, it is clear that the demand is for exclusive use since there is always the possibility of some contamination as containers deteriorate under the physical and chemical actions of the waters involved. As the amount of these wastes is enlarged, which appears to be a certain development, the areas for disposal may become larger and increase the chance that storage may occur in locations considered desirable for other uses. Attempted entry by bottom-crawlers or submersibles into such disposal areas might very well generate conflicting claims.

Beyond the continental shelf, in the area of the deep ocean floor, the use of telechiric craft by one state or group associated with a state could also lead to claims to exclusive authority. Although it is difficult at this stage to anticipate and to describe the context in which this might occur, some speculation suggests possibilities. Thus, if one state were to carve out an area of the ocean floor for exclusive use for a particular purpose or for all purposes, claims might be asserted to exclude any form of foreign intrusion, including various types of telechiric craft, from access for any, or any inconsistent, purpose. The doctrines available for asserting exclusive authority might derive, for example, from analogous claims to limited exclusive authority over high-seas areas for military maneuvers, nuclear testing, and missile experiments. Counterclaims would contend, more or less familiarly, that inclusive access is protected by the doctrine of the freedom of the seas.

The emplacement of submarine installations, manned or unmanned, on the ocean floor could stimulate similar controversies. It is already well known that underwater structures have been adapted to human habitation for brief periods. As technology increasingly improves and as physiological obstacles are surmounted, the possibilities for locating these structures on the ocean floor for extended occupation for a variety of purposes will also improve. Again the major claim is likely to be inclusive, urging that all are free to place these structures on the bed of the sea for whatever purposes believed desirable and that no other state may seek to exclude them. Potential counterclaims here will arise from alleged authority by coastal states over the territorial sea, contiguous zones, and continental shelf, alleging that permanent installations in such areas are incompatible with coastal interests.

The desirability of installing submarine structures on a particular part of the floor of the sea could conceivably also lead to opposing claims of free access. It might be speculated, for example, that one state may seek to "occupy" a sea mount of limited area by emplacing a submarine dwelling and to contend that access to such a sea mount be limited to the first group establishing an installation there. Such contention might be advanced even if the surface of the sea mount could accommodate another installation since it may be thought desirable to preclude the surveillance made possible by close association. It is not known why such a localized area could come to be regarded as so strategic or critical as to justify emplacing a habitable dwelling, but the possibility that preclusive access might thus be asserted, limiting the otherwise acknowledged free access of others, seems worthy of mention.

The operation of conventional military submarines has been suggested as a potential occasion for certain claims to control access even in areas outside the comprehensive authority of any single state. It is common knowledge that both the United States and the Soviet Union maintain large fleets of submarines continuously deployed at sea and prepared for instant military action. Suggestion has been made that these states might wish to establish a submarine surveillance system by which the location of submarines could be plotted as means of increasing their mutual security as, for example, in connection with controls over delivery vehicles for nuclear weapons. Presumably this system would operate not merely within designated areas contiguous to both states but over entire oceans. Anticipation of this possibility has been expressed as follows:

> Under present international law, a submerged submarine outside territorial waters in peace time is not violating any law or amenity, and is not subject to attack. Thus the probability will become steadily greater in the future that an international mischief-maker will be able with impunity to initiate a nuclear holocaust.
>
> It may then become necessary to make a change in international law which would require a submerged submarine to surface and identify itself on demand or be subject to attack. For enforcement of such an international agreement a submarine surveillance system might be essential throughout the high seas.[65]

When nuclear weapons proliferate, as now appears a near certainty, and the two super powers more clearly perceive the common danger, proposals of this kind might become more attractive to both. Perhaps the announcement regarding development of a Chinese Communist submarine fleet will provide impetus to more serious exploration of the possibility of joint action against clandestine methods of delivering weapons.

[65] NAS-NRC, OCEANOGRAPHY 1960–1970, Chapter 10, "International Cooperation" pp. 4–5.

The placing of objects in the water, unmanned but either free-floating or self-propelled, might cause controversy over access. Presently, this claim may be illustrated by the suggested use of buoys for various scientific purposes, such as current measurements. This network of buoys would be employed to gain, record, and communicate information from widely scattered areas of the globe.[66] Since, for scientific purposes, political boundaries are irrelevant, inquiry into the properties of the ocean may make it desirable or even essential to place buoys within areas generally conceded to be within some degree of control by a particular state, as in internal waters, territorial sea, contiguous zones, or over the continental shelf.[67] Coastal states might seek to exclude such objects completely from these areas or perhaps establish acceptable conditions of access that fall short of complete denial. Counterclaims might rest upon a variety of possible propositions, including assertions that buoys designed to gather information about the sea are unique subjects and ought to be given preferred position with respect to access, that buoys in the territorial sea should be treated as analogous to ships in passage and accorded a right of visitation or stay so long as they are not shown to be offensive to coastal interests, and that anywhere beyond the territorial sea a right of access for scientific buoys is fully established under the general rubric of freedom of the seas. The factors suggesting potential difficulty here are that buoys are not ships, hence are not, arguably, entitled to the rights of access accorded ships and that if construction, design, and instrumentation are not properly conceived, buoys might be a navigational hazard in some areas.

Even beyond areas within the comprehensive or more limited authority of a single state, i.e., in the high seas proper, exclusive claims are conceivable. Where very large objects, or groups of objects, are employed as buoys or drifting scientific stations, the claim

---

66 For description of such a program conceived by the U.S. Weather Bureau see *Staff Report on Ocean Buoys*, 1 GEO-MARINE TECHNOLOGY No. 3, p. 41 (Feb., 1965).

67 See generally UNESCO, Intergovernmental Oceanographic Commission, *Preliminary Report of UNESCO and IMCO on the Legal Status of Unmanned and Manned Fixed Oceanographic Stations* (Doc. No. NS/IOC/INF/34) (1962); *id.*, *Report of the Director-General of UNESCO in consultation with the Secretary-General of IMCO on the Legal Status of Oceanographic Research Stations* (Doc. No. UNESCO/IOC/INF-60) (1964). The author is grateful to Commander Larry Parks, Office of the Navy Judge Advocate General, for supplying these documents and relevant unclassified sections of the U.S. delegation reports to IOC meetings.

might be made that the area occupied by them plus a surrounding zone is subject to the exclusive authority of the sponsoring state and that intrusion into the zone or deliberate interference with the objects may be proscribed, and sanctions attached, by national prescriptions. The claim is surely to be anticipated with respect to buoys, of whatever size, that no other state is authorized to interfere deliberately with their operation or hinder the sponsoring state's control over them for the purpose sought.

A final problem about buoys concerns the participant entitled to claim rights in connection with their use. Assuming the nation-state is in some measure protected in location and use of buoys, are international organizations entitled to the same rights of access and enjoyment?

A further source of controversy could reside in the use of self-propelled objects made to move about in response to stimuli from particular characteristics of the environment, thus permitting continuous plotting of various features of the ocean. Since these objects may be free-floating, the potential for conflict lies in the possibility of excluding or interfering with other uses of an area, or for fishing and navigation. Or the devices might intrude into areas alleged, or actually, within the exclusive authority, comprehensive or limited, of another state.

2. Claims to Accommodate Inclusive and Exclusive Access

Another category of claims concerns the chief methods by which states have sought to accommodate their inclusive and exclusive claims to control access to the sea. These have been through the device of establishing boundaries in the ocean, either a boundary fixed in relation to a particular sea area or a boundary enunciated in relation to certain activities occurring there. In some instances, the boundary projected in the past, such as that of the continental shelf, has made reference to both criteria.

The problem to be assessed is whether states will or should seek to alter previously delimited boundaries in response to the new instrumentalities for exploiting the oceans. States might seek, for example, to widen their previously claimed, if not accepted, width for the territorial sea or even internal waters, either in order to achieve exclusive control over newly perceived benefits from the ocean or to seek to minimize newly perceived threats from that source. States might also, in more likely speculation, seek to extend authority for limited purposes beyond state territory as in creation of contiguous zones for objectives not previously considered important. The possibilities with respect to the continental shelf boundary, as with other potential boundary problems in the regions beyond the continental shelf, will be mentioned in connection with the claims about enjoyment of resources.

B. CLAIMS RELATING TO COMPETENCE TO PRESCRIBE AND TO APPLY POLICIES FOR CRAFT MAKING USE OF THE SEA

The subject matter of these claims is usually called "jurisdiction," by which is here meant the competence to prescribe regulations that determine the consequences of interactions and the competence to apply a regulation to a set of events.[68] For the most part, the claims to be made to authority with respect to the new types of ocean vehicles will closely resemble those previously made with respect to conventional sea-going craft, and inherited jurisdictional principles will provide ready guides for responding to such claims. In the following brief discussion, we speculate on possible new claims to competence to prescribe, accompanied by summary statements of the general consensus regarding authority over conventional vessels. There is no discussion of competence to apply since claims to this competence will probably either parallel the claims to prescribe or remain the same as in the past.

1. *Claims Relating to Competence to Prescribe*

a. *Claims Relating to Interactions of Vehicles and Objects Using the Oceans.*

Prevailing expectations about authority over vessels have been summarized as follows:

> For centuries it has been common statement in the authoritative literature that each state has competence to prescribe regulations

[68] See generally McDougal, Lasswell & Vlasic; Law and Public Order in Space 656–748 (1963).

for its own vessels and that no state may, save in accordance with specified exceptions in international law, prescribe regulations for the conduct of the ships of other states. All the traditional sources from which customary international law is inferred . . . yield an abundance of decision and expression to establish the very high authority of this principle.[69]

With the exceptions noted below, the new types of submersible vessels being developed, or already in use, will probably not give rise to new problems in conflicting claims to competence. Whether non-military or military, these vessels can be, and no doubt will be, identified with a particular state in the normal ways, as by registration (attribution of national character) for non-military vessels and by entry on the naval list for military craft.[70] The national character thus impressed upon them will then serve the traditional purposes of such attribution that encompass, in brief, all the procedures that states employ for maintaining shared access to, and productive use of, the sea.[71] In important, if partial, detail, the state whose national character is impressed upon a vessel is regarded as solely competent, in most circumstances, to control the activities of it and as the principal (but not sole) protector of the craft against abuses of authority by other states.

With respect to three of the newer instrumentalities, at least, conflicting claims to competence to prescribe might develop. The establishment of installations on the ocean floor to be inhabited for varying periods; the employment of small submersibles for exploration on continental shelves; and the use of large, uninhabited surface-buoy systems for various purposes, including scientific, military, and commercial, could be responsible for controversy.

Underwater stations resting on the ocean floor can be mobile or immobile, but in either event, disputes over competence to prescribe could arise in particular contexts. Even if coastal states do not object to emplacement of stations beneath adjacent waters outside the territorial sea but on the continental shelf or even outside the continental shelf but still in adjacent waters, there might be demand for compliance with coastal regulations regarding the nature, scope, and duration of the activities to be carried out by the station in the

[69] McDougal & Burke, *op. cit. supra* note 38, at 798.
[70] *Id*. at 1057–61, 1113.
[71] See generally *id.*, ch. 8.

surrounding waters. The sponsoring state might respond, and very probably would in the case of mobile stations such as a submarine resting on the floor, that the structure or craft is to be assimilated to conventional vessels over which the state of national character has sole competence to prescribe while the station is in a high-seas area. The potential use of these stations for scientific purposes in connection with the continental shelf would seem to raise questions of the applicability of the 1958 Continental Shelf Convention, and disputes might turn on interpretation of that instrument.[72] Even more likely, however, to be productive of disputes are the use of underwater stations for direct, if "peaceful," military operations.

Very similar competing claims might be raised in connection with the operation of small submersibles, inhabited or not, in connection with ocean floor exploration. Here, again, demands for coastal competence might be based upon the Continental Shelf Convention. It is possible, too, that new prescriptions might be promulgated in the form of a submerged contiguous zone designed to extend limited authority, even extending to denial of access, for protecting a real or imagined coastal interest from deprivation by the activities of these submersibles. The counterclaim here could be put most strongly, perhaps, in terms of the general expectations, summarized above, concerning the sole competence of the state of registration to control the activities of its vessels.

If conflicting claims emerge in regard to buoy systems, they may arise, initially, because these objects are not inhabited and may not be within the physical control of the sponsoring agency. The significance of these characteristics is, of course, that such objects are susceptible to pilferage, sabotage, or other deliberate destruction. Since the buoys, though perhaps very large, are not considered to be vessels and are not, therefore, registered with a particular state and endowed with a national character, it is possible (though perhaps not likely) that they would be regarded as without protection from interference. Nonetheless, it is reasonable to speculate that the state placing such buoy systems in the water, or whose nationals did so, might seek to prescribe for the protection of such systems,

---

[72] Presumably the argument would be made that scientific investigation, no matter how conducted, was permissible only with coastal consent. It might also be contended that *a fortiori* any submerged station could be excluded by the coastal state no matter what its use.

including stipulations about the inviolability under normal circumstances of the buoy, its instrumentation and associated gear, provisions for responsibility for avoidable but inadvertent damage (as well as for deliberate harm), and sanctions for violation of the regulations so prescribed. Counterclaims might contend that when these objects are placed in the water and beyond the physical control of the sponsoring state or group they are, in the absence of agreement among the states concerned, beyond the protection of exclusively prescribed rules. This contention could be coupled with the assertion that protective regulations must be inclusively prescribed, so that the conditions of liability for damage or destruction are established by states generally rather than by the sponsoring state alone. It seems probable in view of the difficulties of detecting offenders, and of applying sanctions to them, that states will seek general explicit agreement on the protection of these systems.

b) *Claims Relating to Competence to Prescribe for Events on Board Craft or Objects in the Sea*

(1) *Events Affecting Public Order*

The new scientific and technological developments in ocean exploitation do not now appear to suggest any need for claims differing from those made to authority over these events in conventional and familiar situations of ocean use. This allocation has been described as follows:

> In matters relating both to the discipline of the crew and to control of the passengers, it is imperative that the state of national character should have competence immediately to apply its authority. It is the current fashion to refer to the metaphor of the ship as a "floating bit of territory" as outmoded fiction, but as in the famous aphorism, a "fiction feigned is very near the simple truth." The very real community on board a ship is as much in need of the unified prescription and application of authority for the maintenance of public order as a community on land. Every state demands this competence with respect to its ships and in turn recognizes similar competence in other states.[73]

[73] McDougal & Burke, *op. cit. supra* note 38, at 1092.

The new generations of submersible craft would appear very similar to traditional ships in this respect, and the prospective use of fixed underwater stations inhabited for varying periods is certain to require a similar arrangement for controlling events threatening disruptions of public order abroad. The problem is not too dissimilar to that presented by the communities living aboard surface drilling platforms engaged in exploiting the continental shelf. Coastal states have acted to extend some, at least, of the land-based legal system to events on such platforms.[74] It is, hence, less than prescient to anticipate that states will claim a competence to exend relevant legal prescriptions to such events in the new installations. It seems useful, however, presently to direct attention to this potential need for the purpose of avoiding possible uncertainty about authority with respect to this class of objects.

(2) *Events Not Directly Affecting Public Order*

When and if underwater installations become commonplace and are inhabited by relatively large groups for prolonged periods, there will be occasion to provide for the legal consequences of such normal day-to-day interactions as deprivations (torts and crimes), agreements, dispositive acts, and changes of status (births, deaths, marriage, etc.). Although these events may occur in the exotic environment of a building hundreds of feet below the surface of the sea, the problems of legal competence are not likely to present particular difficulty. Many different states may make claim to competence to prescribe the consequences of such interactions, but the established allocations of competence for dealing with these problems in more conventional surroundings will probably provide satisfactory accommodation of conflicts.[75]

C. CLAIMS TO THE ENJOYMENT OF MINERAL RESOURCES

1. *Claims Relating to Whether Resources Are Subject to Exclusive Appropriation*

As with potential resources in outer space, presently even more

[74] For the U.S. see 43 U.S.C. § 1333; for the U.K. see the Continental Shelf Act, 1964, S. 3.

[75] McDougal & Burke, *op. cit. supra* note 38 at 1094–95; McDougal, Lasswell & Vlasic, *op. cit. supra* note 68, at 674–704.

inaccessible than those of the ocean floor, two major types of claims can be envisaged with respect to the mineral resources of the sea.[76] The first, in time, if not in eventual importance, is the assertion by a state that certain resources of an area or *all* resources in a particular area are subject to exclusive appropriation by a single state and that no other state or group may, without consent, have access or even seek access to the resources or area involved. Support for this demand for exclusive access and control will perhaps stem from previous decisions allocating sea resources, notably those underlying the territorial sea and continental shelf. The claim most likely to be contraposed to the demand for exclusivity, though it may be advanced even as a primary claim and not merely as a counterclaim, is that the mineral resources of the sea, either all or certain of them, are open to free access by all who may wish to benefit from them and that no single state or group is authorized, or should be authorized, to acquire exclusive power and dominion over all or any of the mineral resources of the sea. Justification for this position will probably be found in appeals to the ancient doctrine of freedom of the seas according to which, it may be urged, animal resources of the sea have largely been left open to exploitation by all comers.

Claims to exclusive access will probably, in more detail, be limited both geographically and temporally. The ocean is a vast area, and with the known quantities of some minerals on the ocean floor, the claim to exclusive use might include only a relatively small area and only for a term of years. One suggestion is that a 100 mile square area might be large enough to provide adequate return on investment, if uninterrupted exploitation can thereby be secured. Since minerals are found in areas far larger than this, there would appear to be no necessity for conflict between exclusive claims. Where, however, minerals were located in a small, uniquely advantageous area, which was not duplicated elsewhere, there would be potential for controversy in the absence of agreed upon criteria for exclusive appropriation.

For completeness of reference, if not for cogent speculation, it is necessary to mention the possible claim that the mineral resources of the deep ocean floor have already been allocated by the Conti-

[76] The categorization of claims here is the same as that employed for space resources in McDougal, Lasswell & Vlasic, *op. cit. supra* note 68, at 770–74.

nental Shelf Convention of 1958.[77] This claim would contend that the definition of the shelf incorporated therein is flexible and that the area of exclusive coastal control extends outward to the limits of all exploitation, including the mining of surficial sea-floor sediments. The counterclaim in reply would concede that the shelf is defined by treaty in terms of the depth at which exploitation is possible, but would observe that the situation envisaged at Geneva did not include the possibilities now emerging in deep ocean-floor mining. Furthermore, it could be argued in reply, the policies that supported the allocation of the adjacent shallow submarine regions to the adjacent state for certain purposes are not, at least not obviously, pertinent to allocation of the deep ocean floor to states adjoining on that ocean. Hence, there is no reason to regard the broad language of the Continental Shelf Convention as necessarily incorporating the general expectation that the deeper areas are to be allocated to adjoining, but non-adjacent, states. All this could be buttressed by attempts at persuasive demonstration that the policies at stake in allocating the minerals of the deep sea bed are very different from those involved with the adjacent shallow areas.

2. *Claims with Respect to Modality of Establishing Exclusive Appropriation*

Although it may be assumed that certain resources may be regarded as subject to exclusive appropriation, controversy may still be engendered by conflicting claims concerning the modality by which a claim may be established. Claims to exclusive appropriation may rest upon discovery or symbolic acts, effective occupation and use, or contiguity. Claims on the first of these grounds have not been frequent recently with respect to any resource and have never been accepted in practice. Claims to land resources put forward on the basis of effective occupation and use are, of course, very familiar and constitute the chief method by which exclusive appropriation

---

[77] *But see* MERO, THE MINERAL RESOURCES OF THE SEA 289 (1965); "Presumably also, the continental shelf can be extended by the coastal nation out over the edge of the geologic shelf, down the continental slope and on out over the deep ocean floor to whatever point a commercial minerals dredge can operate. Such an extension was probably not the intention of the Conference, but the wording of the articles of the Fourth Convention is so clear as to leave little room for maneuvering on this point."

of resources has been established. Contiguity, as the foundation for a claim to exclusive appropriation, has also been advanced without marked success in acquiring land resources but has been honored in somewhat greater degree for ocean resources.

D. CLAIMS TO ENJOYMENT OF ANIMAL RESOURCES

1. *Claims to Inclusive and Exclusive Access*

The advancement of demands for use of marine animal resources range from complete exclusivity, rejecting any exploitation of a particular area or resource by nationals of another, to the polar extreme of complete inclusivity, asserting commonly that all peoples may share in exploitation without limitation. Within these limits states assert claims with varying degrees of inclusivity and exclusivity.[78]

Claims to exclusive access are made in terms both of areas and of particular resources. Each coastal state lays claim to exclusive access to all adjacent animal resources by reason of their more comprehensive claim to the territorial sea. Beyond the territorial sea, exclusivity is sometimes also demanded in the establishment of a contiguous zone for fishing purposes. In the submarine regions, states seek exclusive access to the animal resources of the ocean floor by assertion of authority over continental shelf resources.

Demands for sole exploitation of a particular animal resource or resources take the form of an outright claim to ownership, as in the United States assertion regarding fur seals in the nineteenth century, or as a preferential position in an international conservation scheme. This latter claim is illustrated by the International North Pacific agreement in the exploitation of halibut and salmon. The same type of claim is more generally made in the demands for preference or priority for a coastal state when multistate exploitation of a particular fishing stock or stocks is subjected to regulation.

Inclusive access to marine animal resources is urged in terms of the doctrine of freedom of the seas. The common assertion of claim is that the nationals of each state must be permitted free access to fishing resources and that they cannot be forbidden such access, nor can it be qualified, without the agreement of the state concerned.

[78] See generally McDougal & Burke, *op. cit. supra* note 38, at 923–27.

Accommodation of access concerns both exclusive and inclusive claims. In the first instance, states must seek to reconcile claims to exclusive access with claims to inclusive. This is sought chiefly by the method of establishing various boundaries in the sea. Thus the claims to delimitation of the areas of internal waters and territorial sea, by providing for the base line for the territorial sea and by setting a width for the latter, are a method for determining both the areas within which the coastal state claims exclusive disposition of resources and the areas within which the general community may have uninhibited access. Beyond the territorial sea, but similarly affected by delimitation of the base line inclosing internal waters, the establishment of a certain contiguous zone may also delimit areas of inclusive and exclusive access. Finally, the areas asserted to be part of the continental shelf may be alleged to determine the sharability of certain animal resources connected with the shelf or in the water above it. And in this special instance of shelf animal resources, claims to exclusive access are also made in terms of the definition of the animal resources that a state claims to be in a certain relationship with the shelf. Illustration of this claim may be seen, for example, in the United States contention that king crabs are a shelf resource exploitable solely by Americans and in the claim by Brazil that lobsters on its shelf area are exploitable solely by Brazilians.

Necessity for accommodation between conflicting claims may also arise from common insistence upon inclusive access to a resource. The problem occurs, as is well known, because free entry to a fishery has the effect of permitting virtually unrestrained exploitation by all participants in the fishery. If fishermen cannot be assured that their own restraint in exploiting a resource will achieve any proposed goal of limitation since others may enter the fishery at will, there is no incentive to accept limitations on fishing effort. This situation may lead either to demands for sole use by one participant, as some states allegedly seek through widening of the territorial sea, or to the creation of a contiguous zone for fishing, or to efforts for establishing a regulatory scheme binding on all actual and potential participants. As part of this scheme some states have demanded a priority in access for a particular state.

2. *Claims to Competence over Access to Fishery Resources*

Claims about competence to decide who gets access to what fishery resources are also both exclusive and inclusive. Some states, for example, assert not only a demand for sole access to a particular fishery but also contend that such access may be established unilaterally. In this view, the decision about the permissibility of unilateral enjoyment is also unilateral.[79]

Most claims are, however, that decisions about access must be made inclusively, i.e., that unilateral enjoyment can only be established in accordance with a general consensus in the community. The most important demands in recent years for enlarging the area of exclusive fishing have incorporated also the claim that the permissibility of enlargement is decided by an inclusive process of decision.

That most claims to prescribe and apply policy in this area of concern are inclusive, and that each state commonly asserts sole authority over its own vessels, are, however, the occasions giving rise to the most intractable problem involving ocean resources. How does the community or an individual state establish a system for regulating exploitation if no one state has any authority over all those involved? The problem, in other words, is to create a structure of authority that will assure orderly, peaceful, and economical use of the resources of the sea.

A principal goal of the present discussion is to seek an approach to this problem by suggesting a fruitful means of describing previous efforts at establishing international organizations concerned with fishery conservation and of indicating some factors that might be taken into account in future efforts.

E. CLAIMS RELATING TO THE ADMINISTRATION OF SHARED USE

Since the new practices in exploring and exploiting the oceans will continue to permit a significant degree of sharing in participation with others and yet have a high degree of collective impact, it can be expected that demands will be forthcoming for explicit multi-

[79] McDougal & Burke, *op. cit. supra* note 38, at 486–87.

lateral agreements establishing the conditions and consequences of interaction. Among the activities that seem likely to call for an accommodation that demands multilateral prescription are the employment of buoys of different kinds for various purposes; the establishment of communications between surface objects and others (including with those in the space above and with both surface and subsurface objects); the establishment of underwater communications conducted for underwater operations (including navigation); the disposal of wastes; the conduct of scientific experiments; the operation of subsurface installations; the pursuit of scientific investigations; and the acquisition and management of sharable and non-sharable resources. Brief mention of these possibilities seems warranted.

The major legal problems about buoys that calls for explicit regulation, other than the claims about access already mentioned, include access to the equipment on the buoys and to the data collected by it, protection of the buoy system and shipping through appropriate notices, markings and lights, and liability for interference with the buoy system and for harm caused by it.[80]

The communications networks required for the newly intensified use and study of the sea must, of course, be meshed with other demands for space in the radio spectrum. The international procedures for dealing with this problem area are already well established and in frequent use so that this is not a novel difficulty nor one that should require the development of new institutions or practices. In one aspect, however, the ocean communications problem may be unique; and that is in the development of entirely submerged communications systems. Whether or when this type of communication becomes an international problem perhaps depends primarily upon the emergence of submarine transportation as an economic mode of commercial transport. When and if that time arrives, it will probably be necessary to arrange for allocations of the frequencies, stations, and, perhaps, depths that will be used by the participating states in establishing a communications and navigation system for the submerged vehicles.

Problems of waste disposal, including especially radioactive materials, are and have been under constant scrutiny in the inter-

---

[80] See sources cited *supra* note 67.

national arena.[81] States have already joined in efforts to eliminate one of the major sources of pollution, that caused by oil.[82] As the ocean becomes a more inviting place for storage of radioactive wastes, which seems to be most likely as the quantities increase, concerted action to minimize undesirable effects may be widely demanded. Insistence on inclusive regulation of this form of inter-action may be further inspired as participants widen the range and form of their multiple uses of the sea. The widely expected, or at least hoped for, increase in food productivity, for example, will surely focus increased attention on possibilities of contamination from radioactive substances, as will also, of course, successful estab-lishment of human habitations under the sea.

Mutual accommodation by explicit agreement would appear necessary in providing for the safety of such underwater installa-tions as states and private associations employ for pursuing their objectives in the sea. In the beginning, at least, subsurface structures may require attendance or surveillance by observers on the surface; hence navigation problems may revolve around the conventional necessity for avoiding collisions. But as more sophisticated equip-ment and procedures are devised and surface assistance can be dispensed with, protection may require the use of large surface buoys or others means of signaling the presence of underwater objects. It is perhaps not beyond the realm of probability that a system of registration will be devised as a means of disseminating information about the location of underwater buildings.

At present, scientific co-operation in carrying out study of the sea is largely organized through private associations of scientists, but in the future it could be desirable to provide a more formal organization. In fact, of course, the beginning of such a mechanism exists in the form of the Intergovernmental Oceanographic Com-mission.

The management of sharable and non-sharable resources is an area in which it is already quite clear that explicit inclusive arrange-ments are a critical requirement. For resources that are sharable, the

[81] International Atomic Energy Agency, *Radioactive Waste Disposal into the Sea passim* (1961); Convention on the High Seas, Article 25.

[82] Convention for the Prevention of Pollution, United Nations Legislative Series, *Supplement to Laws and Regulations on the Regime of the High Seas and Laws Concerning the Nationality of Ships* 33 (U.N. Doc. No. ST/LEG/SER. B/8) (1959).

problems of economic use are abundantly illustrated by the difficulties encountered in fishery exploitation. We have already had some experience in attempting to resolve these problems, though it would be a gross overstatement to say that the efforts have met with a great measure of success. Even resources to be regarded as non-sharable, meaning those in which some measure of exclusive right to access is honored, will very likely require multilateral agreement. Thus, it seems probable that there will be some, perhaps even many ocean resources that can be exploited economically only on condition of recognizing a degree of exclusive appropriation. Even if simple priority in time is recognized as decisive of who may appropriate resources, there will probably still be a need for agreement on how to accommodate exploitative operations with other, potentially conflicting, uses of the sea.

CHAPTER   III

PROCESS OF DECISION

The two types of decision comprising the total flow of decisions called international law, the constitutive and the particular, appear certain to undergo varying degrees of change in response to innovations in the specific processes of interaction and claim concerning the ocean. The constitutive process of decision, the process by which the general community establishes the basic structure for international decision-making, embraces all phases of the decision process including decision-makers, objectives, base values, arenas, strategies, and outcomes.[83] The particular decisions made are those in response to specific controversies over exploration and use of the sea.[84] The following discussion attempts brief preliminary speculation, seeking both to identify potential changes in some aspects of the constitutive process of decision as it pertains to events on the ocean and to recall the principles and techniques inherited from more conventional periods in the history of ocean exploitation, that decision-makers have employed for resolving some disputes about particular claims that might be used, rationally or not, in the future.

[83] For comprehensive discussion see McDOUGAL, LASSWELL & VLASIC, *op. cit. supra* note 68, at 94–137.
[84] This aspect of the decision process is more fully examined in McDOUGAL & BURKE, *op. cit. supra* note 38, *passim.*

A. CONSTITUTIVE PROCESS OF AUTHORITATIVE DECISION

1. *Authoritative Decision-makers*

Nation-state officials have long been the most important decision-makers in the law of the sea; and, barring major change in prevailing expectations, they will continue to be of the most consequence in performing critical decision functions. It seems probable that even if the new possibilities of intensified ocean use are limited initially to a relatively few states, the representatives of all states will expect to have a voice in projecting new legal prescriptions, or altering the old, for dealing with emerging problems. Nonetheless, marked influence on choice will reside in the few states whose capabilities in exploitation are most advanced.[85]

Among other participants in authoritative decisions, international governmental organizations are of the more recent additions and have already had significant roles to play.[86] The existence of the United Nations was probably indispensable to the formulation of the Geneva Conventions on the law of the sea, for without the focus and continuity provided by such a forum it is doubtful whether the outcome could have been realized against the inertia of numerous states. And, of course, it was a subsidiary organ of the General Assembly of the United Nations, the International Law Commission, whose extensive efforts produced the drafts that formed the bases of discussion for the conference convened in Geneva in 1958. Other specialized agencies, particularly the FAO, also contributed to the background work of the 1958 Conference as well as in a continuing role as collectors and disseminators of information useful for legal purposes. One such specialized agency, the Intergovernment Maritime Consultative Organization, is devoted wholly to certain maritime matters and others, including UNESCO, ITU, and WMO, have limited competences in connection with the oceans.

Among the less universal international organizations prominent in the decision process relating to the ocean are the various con-

---

[85] Observers frequently emphasize this factor in recommendations urging greater support for ocean science and technology. See, e.g., *Hearings, supra* note 9, at 100, 119.

[86] One prominent observer estimates that the need for co-operation on the ocean is alone sufficient to require an organization such as the United Nations and the specialized agencies. Chapman, *Hearings, supra* note 9, at 137.

servation organizations established to deal with marine fisheries. Only relatively few states belong to one or another of these groups, and, in general, the decision-making competence conferred upon them is minimal.

Private associations, national and international, specialized, in particular, in achieving wealth and enlightenment or, representing certain skills and interest groups, have long been active in influencing various official participants. As with similar groups in space exploration, scientific bodies concerned with the ocean will have a continually stronger role as the ocean becomes more evidently a critical area of interaction for a variety of endeavors.

Even the private individual, who only exceptionally has significant influence in the decision process, may occasionally, by force of personality or intellectual contribution, have impact on the flow of decisions.

2. *Objectives*

It seems unlikely that decision-makers will discontinue their efforts to achieve common interests as activities in exploitation of the oceans are intensified. Moreover, there is nothing in the perceivable future to indicate that recognition of interdependencies in use of the ocean will be obscured; indeed this recognition is much more likely to become clearer as the conditions of ocean exploitation are more intimately affected by each participant's activities. Nevertheless, the degree or extent to which decision-makers can act to achieve their recognizable common interests in peaceful and productive uses of the sea depend on many factors, particularly those pertaining to expectations of violence prevalent at critical times. The fact of the matter is that, at least in the intermediate run, the ocean is too critical and strategic in calculations of relative strength to permit full or even substantial deference to the accomplishment of some common objectives. In short, effective realization of common, widely recognized interests in the use and control of the sea depends on a much wider constellation of factors than those immediately concerned with this area.

3. *Arenas*

Whatever the impact of expectations of violence on wider perspectives about authority over the ocean, even the experience of the past few years establishes that more organized inclusive arenas of decision can be, and will be, employed for making decisions about relatively important disputes over access to, and enjoyment of, the sea. In the past, the vast majority of important decisions responding to controversies over use and control of the sea were made in totally unorganized arenas. What we call international law consisted (and, for the most part, consists to this day) of inferences of legality drawn from uniformities in the behavior of states and other participants.[87] As noted above in relation to participants, the establishment of the United Nations and its subordinate organs and components, especially the International Law Commission, has already provided a somewhat more highly organized arena for making decisions. The work of the specialized agencies, the FAO, the ITU, the IMCO, and UNESCO, though it has not been in the exercise of any comprehensive competence with respect to the sea, does provide some experience with inclusive, organized structures of authority. Tentative beginnings, and no more than that, have been made in the marine conservation field toward establishing inclusive arenas of decision. It seems eminently safe to assume that the competences of all these groups in regulating events on the oceans will either be enlarged, or, perhaps in addition, new organized arenas will be devised for facilitating performance of various decision functions.

4. Bases of Power

Since the most important decisions about the oceans are still made by states in a decentralized arena of decision, it should occasion no surprise to find that state officials retain exclusive control over the most potent bases of power and have been reluctant to confer, except sporadically, significant values on international organizations.

The extent to which organized structures of authoritative decision are deprived of support for decision-making is amply indicated by the minimal formal authority conferred upon them or, if ample authority is conferred, by the minimum effectiveness that they can exercise. Not a single such group, including the United Nations,

[87] See McDougal, Lasswell & Vlasic, *op. cit. supra* note 68, at 115–19 for discussion of the requirements for establishing customary international law.

possesses, in prevailing expectation, any significantly comprehensive competence to prescribe or apply policy. Indeed, very recent experience indicates a diminution in capacity for effective action regarding vital problems.

It would, however, be clearly inaccurate to conclude that organized arenas of inclusive decision are devoid of bases of power, including formal authority. Authority conferred does include, in relation to the oceans, important roles in the performance of the decision functions of intelligence, recommendation, and appraisal. Moreover, with respect to other values, the international organizations with responsibilities relating to the sea are able to use control over enlightenment and skill as sometimes potent bases of power. The task of collecting and analyzing data regarding social, economic, and scientific problems of international significance and of disseminating information can serve to focus attention of effective power holders upon problems of legal significance and might have a measurable impact upon the decision-makers charged with recommending, prescribing, applying, or terminating regulations.

It remains to record the hypothesis that if contemporary trends in ocean use make for greater interdependency among participants in that use, the tendency will be to confer more assets upon the international organization that will be found necessary for effective regulation.

B. PARTICULAR DECISIONS

1. *Claims Relating to Access*

a. *Claims to Inclusive and Exclusive Access*

The substantive law relative to specific claims and counterclaims, the general principles established in past experience that could possibly be employed for resolving future problems, can be briefly summarized. It will be quickly evident that the principles accommodating inclusive and exclusive access are largely those applicable to areas near land masses, a feature due principally to the fact that disputes over access have arisen chiefly in the more restricted water areas near coasts. Beyond these adjacent seas, the predominant principle has been expressed in the venerable doctrine of freedom of the seas, both enjoining that all states are entitled to free access to the sea with sole control over vessels allocated to the state of its nationality and prohibiting any comprehensive exclusive authority over access to any other state. It is true, of course, that even in non-contiguous high seas, states have sought and, in the view of some, obtained the authority to exclude access by foreign vessels to particular water areas. Illustrative of these decisions are the demands by the major powers (the United States, the Soviet Union, and the United Kingdom) for exclusive use of huge ocean areas for the testing of nuclear weapons, and the response revealed by the behavior of the other states.

In the waters most immediately adjacent to the land, the part called internal waters, states in their traditional practice have honored a completely exclusive and comprehensive authority in the coastal state to forbid the entry of foreign vessels at the discretion of the coastal state.[88] In very recent times, as the area of internal waters has been expanded by international agreement, there has also been explicit agreement that in certain parts of internal waters, namely the high seas and territorial sea inclosed as internal waters by a newly established straight baseline system, foreign vessels are protected in a right of access the same as that honored by the doctrine of innocent passage that previously was associated with the territorial sea.

This general recognition of a right of passage through the territorial sea, if innocent, has been the chief doctrinal method by which states have sought to accommodate the common inclusive interest in a free movement on the oceans with the common exclusive interest in protecting each state from sea-based deprivations.[89] All states have thus been enabled to make efficient use of the sea for transportation and communication, while the coastal state could preclude access when threats appeared of harm to important coastal interests. The recent authoritative formulation of doctrine in the Territorial Sea Convention of 1958 expresses this balance of interests by first acknowledging a right of innocent passage and then defining innocent to mean passage which "is not prejudicial to the

---

[88] See generally McDougal & Burke, *op. cit. supra* note 38, 99–126.
[89] *Id.* at 187–269 examines community policy and the trend of decisions regarding this problem of access.

peace, good order or security of the coastal State."[90] In confirmation of the special weight that this rather vague language appears to place on coastal interests, a subsequent section provides that under certain limited conditions, involving demands of military security, the coastal state may suspend all passage through a specified part of the territorial sea.[91] Since this article provides that such portions may not include areas of the territorial sea forming a strait,[92] it seems clear that inclusive interests in free access were not disregarded.

Submarines are especially provided for in the convention in regard to access to the territorial sea. Apparently reflecting the practical circumstance that historically submarines have always been military instrumentalities, it is provided that such vessels must travel on the surface when transiting the territorial sea.[93] Presumably, a submarine making a submerged passage would not be considered innocent and could be excluded from passage or, perhaps, even destroyed if exclusionary measures were of no avail. Contemporary events suggest that discovery of an unidentified submarine in national waters can occasion drastic measures by the coastal state.

In the surface waters immediately adjacent to the territorial sea, coastal controls honored by international law have historically included, in recognition of the common exclusive interest in protection of internal social processes of the coastal state, some measure of authority over access by foreign vessels.[94] Although not without controversy, coastal states have often asserted a competence, limited in both duration and purpose, to control access to waters variously distant from the land and beyond the territorial sea. But recent decision, embodied in multilateral international agreement, appears to have placed stringent, and in the view of some, undesirable, restrictions on coastal authority to limit or condition access to contiguous zones. Thus, the 1958 Convention on the Territorial Sea and Contiguous Zones, in Article 24, seems largely, if not completely, to preclude consequential coastal competence to prescribe or apply policy in contiguous zones. The dimensions of the author-

[90] Article 14(4).
[91] Article 16(3).
[92] Article 16(4).
[93] Article 14(6).
[94] McDOUGAL & BURKE, *op. cit. supra* note 38, 582–607 discusses community policy and decisions.

ity remaining in states do not seem entirely clear, and it seems uncertain whether the limitation on authority embodied in Article 24 will survive the legitimate demands of states in protecting their common exclusive interests.

Also, beyond the territorial sea and overlapping the regime of contiguous zones as envisaged by the 1958 Convention, the waters superjacent to the continental shelf have recently become subject, in accordance with widely accepted principles of international law, to a measure of exclusive authority over access. The more precise content of these prescriptions was the subject of debate at the 1958 Geneva Conference and was clarified in some detail in the Convention on the Continental Shelf produced at the conference and now in force between states parties to it, including the United States. It was, of course, obvious (though not without controversy) long before the Geneva Conference met in 1958 that if the general community was to honor any access to the mineral resources of the continental shelf, requiring structures extending above the surface, that some, perhaps substantial on occasion, restriction on free access to the surface of the sea must be conceded.[95] Moreover, since the pattern of claim after the initial United States proclamation in 1945 quickly established that coastal states were to be conceded their demand for exclusive access, it became recognized that restrictions on inclusive access were to be determined exclusively, i.e., by each state acting unilaterally with a minimum of review by other states or by the organized community of states. Hence, it caused no surprise when the Geneva Conference concluded with almost universal support that on the continental shelf each state has "sovereign rights for the purpose of exploring it and exploiting its natural resources."[96] This means, clearly, that even substantial interference with inclusive access to the area for purposes of movement may be justified on occasion in carrying out exclusive activities on the shelf.

Beyond these rather general references to "sovereign rights" for specified purposes and the more specific accommodation in later provision of the named rights with navigation, fishing, and scientific investigation,[97] the convention does not deal directly with

---

[95] See, e.g., Lauterpacht, *Sovereignty over Submarine Areas,* 27 Brit. Yb. Int'l. Law 376, 402–03 (1950).

[96] Convention on the Continental Shelf, Article 2(1).

[97] Article 5.

future conflicting claims to access, but it is certainly implied, and no doubt did not seem worthy of mention, that access to the ocean bottom for whatever purpose would be subject to exclusive coastal authority similar to that honored over the indicated surface operations.

On the high seas, beyond territorial sea, contiguous zones and continental shelf, states enjoy the greatest measure of freedom of movement, although even in these vast expanses some exclusive restraints on inclusive access are honored in exceptional instances. Here again, as in contiguous zones, the extent of exclusive authority is not beyond controversy. There is, nonetheless, a considerable record of acquiescence, not accorded merely as a matter of courtesy but in recognition of legal requirement, in assertions by states of authority to control access by foreign vessels to these areas of the high seas.[98]

b) *Accommodations of Inclusive and Exclusive Access*

The final set of doctrines that decision-makers use to resolve controversies over access are concerned with delimitation of the familiar "zones" of authority: internal waters,[99] territorial sea,[100] contiguous zones,[101] and continental shelf.[102] It is familiar history that the response by decision-makers to controversies about access have sometimes been framed in terms of principles for the delimitation of various zones of authority. For example, the Anglo-Norwegian Fisheries Case was essentially concerned with the issue of access to fisheries resources, rather than with use of the sea as a spatial extension resource; but the International Court of Justice (in addition to others) also offered as a major justification for its approval of the Norwegian straight baseline system, creating new areas of internal waters, that factors relating to movement and navigation may warrant the inclosure of certain areas within internal waters. And, of course, some demands at the Geneva conferences of 1958 and 1960 for a wider territorial sea rested upon assertions of a need to control the access of vessels to and aircraft over the waters adjacent to a state.

98 See McDougal & Burke, *op. cit. supra* not 38, at 751–94.
99 See generally *id*. at 305–445.
100 *Id*. at 446–564.
101 *Id*. at 597, 605–06.
102 *Id*. at 663–91; 724–30.

2. *Claims Relating to Competence to Prescribe*

a) *Claims Relating to Interactions of Vehicles and Objects Using the Oceans*

In previous discussion, it was convenient to make quick summary of the inherited jurisdictional principles that are probably suitable for most of the claims to prescribe regarding new kinds of vessels and instrumentalities; hence, discussion is now limited to brief mention of treaty provisions and certain customary prescriptions to which decision-makers could, or might, turn in seeking guidance for resolving controversies about more difficult problems. The 1958 Continental Shelf Convention, the Convention on the Territorial Sea and Contiguous Zone, and, perhaps, customary prescriptions concerning authority over contiguous zones, all might be thought relevant to claims about underwater stations or the new types of submersibles. In the following, it is intended only to note that these various prescriptions could be employed by decision-makers seeking to resolve controverted claims regarding these instrumentalities. It is not now sought to clarify policies for their application, nor to make detailed description of apparently analogous previous decisions, nor to attempt predictions of detailed application in specific contexts.

Certain of the more general provisions of the Continental Shelf Convention, as well as seemingly more specific articles, are relevant in connection with claims over activities on the shelf and in the waters above. Of the general provisions, the most important is Article 2(1), which confers upon coastal states "sovereign rights" over the continental shelf "for the purpose of exploring it and exploiting its natural resources." Article 2(2) confirms the exclusiveness of the rights involved by explicitly declaring that if the coastal state does not explore or exploit the shelf, no one else may do so without coastal consent. The significance of these provisions is in their potential for authorizing interference with exploration of the shelf, including activities of substantial scientific merit as well as of commercial or miliary value. The form and nature of such restrictions cannot, of course, be identified in detail, but it is possible to envisage conditions or limitations with undesirable effects such as, for example, excessive license fees, unreasonable stipulations about permissible areas of work, and onerous regulations concerning time of work, equipment, and personnel. Moreover, the breadth of Articles 1 and 2 might be used to justify even restraints upon activity in the waters above the shelf.

Subsequent provisions in the convention deal more specifically with the relation between coastal authority over the shelf and certain critical activities, namely navigation, fishing, conservation, and scientific research. With respect to the former three operations, "interference," apparently referring to physical obstacles, is permissible if it is not "unjustifiable." But with respect to scientific research, no interference is permissible, subject to the condition that the research is "carried out with the intention of open publication." It is somewhat difficult to understand what this latter prohibition on interference might mean, especially in light of still another provision dealing expressly with research. Article 5(8) states:

> The consent of the coastal state shall be obtained in respect of any research concerning the shelf and undertaken there. Nevertheless, the coastal state shall not normally withhold its consent if the request is submitted by a qualified institution with a view to purely scientific research into the physical or biological characteristics of the continental shelf, subject to the proviso that the coastal state shall have the right if it so desires, to participate or be represented in the research, and that in any event the results shall be published.

Apparently this provision is intended to have a limited application, i.e., only to "research concerning the continental shelf and undertaken there" and not to research concerning the waters above. Unfortunately, if this supposed distinction is not an operational one, and it seems suspiciously neat considering the physical and biological interdependencies involved, the result could be that decision-makers might feel inclined to extend coastal competence to prescribe to all research in the shelf area, including that carried on by submersibles and other instrumentalities in the waters above the floor.

Potential authority for extending coastal competence to prescribe for interactions involving foreign craft and stations in areas adjacent to the territorial sea might also be sought, and perhaps found, in the customary prescriptions on contiguous zones.[103] Here, how-ever, as noted above in connection with decisions about access, the Convention on the Territorial Sea and Contiguous Zone in Article 24 appears to limit coastal competence severely. Despite the restric-tion, it is worth recalling that states are still authorized to extend authority beyond state territory for security purposes and future decision-makers perhaps would look to this authority to establish coastal competence with respect to certain military activities in nearby sea areas. It may be added also that the traditional flexible concept of the contiguous zone, apparently interred by Article 24 of the Territorial Sea Convention, may suddenly be revived to cope with demands created by hitherto unimagined uses of the sea.

3. *Enjoyment of Mineral Resources*

It has been over fifteen years since lawyers interested in the law about exploitation of marine oil deposits were reminded that the process of decision, even in the traditional international law of the sea, contained two parallel streams of principles by which contro-versies over access to such marine resources might be resolved.[104] One, usually considered the predominant principle, emphasizes free-dom of access for all who wish to compete in exploitation. Formu-lated in terms of the doctrine of freedom of the seas, this principle would, if projected into the future development of ocean resources, honor inclusive and unorganized access to resources. The sharing of use protected by international law would emerge from the unpatterned joint activities of many different entrepreneurs acting on the ocean. The similarity to the regime for exploitation of fishery resources is obvious.

Another set of principles, more recently evolved but no less authoritative, is designed to honor exclusive (though common) interests of coastal states and would, in the context of mineral exploitation, concede exclusive access to a certain area to one state, whether coastal or not. It is now familiar to all that despite some challenge to the allocation of exclusive access to coastal states, the general community adopted this principle for allocating many, but not all, of the mineral and animal resources of the continental shelf

---

[103] Discussion of these prescriptions and citations of literature are in *id*. at 584–603.

[104] See Lauterpacht, *supra* note 95, at 403–08.

by conferring on the coastal states "sovereign rights" for exploration and exploitation of such resources. Moreover, the definition of the continental shelf for the purpose of this allocation was left open-ended so that it might be expanded outward as exploitation became feasible in deeper waters.

The primary question posed by these alternatives in inherited principle is not hard to perceive. It is whether either of these sets of principles, establishing patterns of exploitation in certain contexts, will serve community policies as new areas or new resources are opened to exploitation by advancing technology and, if not, what other principles and procedures can be devised or adapted as practicable and desirable courses of action. The suddenness with which exploitation possibilities are being surveyed in the deeper ocean, beyond the continental shelf, coupled with the contributions of those interested in opening undersea areas to direct human access, quite clearly call for more intensive examination of this problem than has been deemed desirable or useful in the past.

In addition to examination of previous experience with ocean resources, inquiry should include comparative survey of principal techniques employed by the major legal systems for allocating mineral resources on land.

It is not now intended to attempt detailed clarification of community policies at stake with respect to mineral exploitation. Some comment should, nevertheless, be made concerning principles available from past experience. It seems clear that similarities and dissimilarities between previously exploited ocean resources and those yet to be exploited might be critical for the supposed usefulness of previously accepted principles for allocating rights of exploitation. Mineral resources found on the ocean floor, or most prominently mentioned (such as manganese nodules), can both be compared with and contrasted to fishery resources.[105] The latter occur in tremendous numbers and are mostly self-replenishing. The manganese nodules also are found in vast quantities, estimated in the trillions of tons, distributed rather thinly over equally vast areas of the ocean floor. Moreover, these nodules are as a whole prob-

---

[105] Mero, The Mineral Resources of the Sea (1965) is a comprehensive account of these resources and the technology and economics of their exploitation. See especially 284–93 for reference to legal problems and information relevant thereto.

ably self-replenishing, since the rate of exploitation probably will be exceeded by the rate of formation. But the nodules are not in movement and the costly equipment to take them must, even if mobile, be concentrated on the resources of a relatively fixed area. Fishing vessels, of course, must be highly mobile, at least under present technology, in order to fit the characteristics of the prey. The same stock of fish can be, or has been, fairly regularly, subjected to simultaneous fishing by vessels of different states in the same ocean area as well as in different parts of the sea, and fishing so conducted can still be a profitable enterprise. But this same arrangement might not work for the ocean mining industry. Mr. John Mero, a leader in the study of the feasibility of ocean mining, has emphasized that a major feature distinguishing mining from fishing is that the miner has an investment in the mineral deposit he is working or even proposing to work;[106] this is not usually the case with fishermen though it sometimes can be. The occasion for the investment in the potential mine is that the feasibility of mining various deposits differs greatly, dependent on a considerable number of factors, and very careful studies must be made to determine which of several sites should be worked. The mining system employed will then be designed for efficient operation at the site chosen.[107] It is, hence, easy to see that the mining operator has an interest in securing exclusive access to a particular location. Without more, these considerations appear to mean that provision for free access to ocean mineral resources must be accompanied by a system for recognizing exclusive rights in limited areas. Such recognition would, presumably, permit profitable operation at the same time that it affords virtually unlimited access to the same or similar resources elsewhere.[108] It is, of course, possible that for the initial mining ventures, the need for international legal protection will be minimal. If exclusive access is needed, it may be assured by virtue of the unique technological capabilities of the new enterprise as well, possibly, as by control over, or access to, markets.

[106] *Id.* at 291–92.

[107] *Ibid.*

[108] Gain would perhaps continue to be achieved so long as excessive entry into exploitation is avoided. If entry is open and easily effected, the same problems experienced by fishermen would apparently soon develop. See CHRISTY, EFFICIENCY IN THE USE OF MARINE RESOURCES 6 (RFF Reprint No. 49) (Sept., 1964).

4. *Enjoyment of Animal Resources*

The bitterest peacetime controversies about the sea have focused upon conflicting claims to access for fishery resources. Here, again, decisions over the centuries have sought to protect the interests of both coastal and non-coastal states (so termed in relation to the fishery resources concerned). Some degree of exclusive access has been protected through recognition of exclusive authority over access to certain waters adjacent to the state. Traditionally these were the areas of internal water, such as bays and gulfs of certain dimension and size, and the territorial sea of modest width, usually about three miles. More recently exclusive access has been permitted increasingly in even larger areas as international law comes to recognize new methods of delimitation of sea areas. Illustrative are the employment of the straight baseline system that has become widespread after the Anglo-Norwegian Fisheries Case and after inclusion of the system in the provisions of the 1958 Convention on the Territorial Sea and Contiguous Zone and the creation of new areas of exclusive access through use of the venerable contiguous zone concept.

At the same time as these various devices and principles were molded as a means of adjustment to the pressure for more extensive fishing rights, the hoary doctrine of freedom of the seas, connoting in this context free access to the fishery resources of the high seas, continued to be invoked to permit anyone who so wished to enter into exploitation. The prevalence of this general principle about access to fisheries occupies a central place among the factors contributing to the difficulties of establishing and maintaining a regime of rational exploitation of these resources.[109] For whatever expansions have occurred in areas of exclusive fishery rights, or in techniques for securing such rights even outside exclusive areas of the sea, the regions generally accepted as open to unrestricted entry by fishermen are still very large and offer great potential for increasing future fishery productivity. In this vast area, states and other participants still consider freedom of the seas a doctrinal means of claiming an unrestricted right to participate in a fishery and, as a principle, commanding decision-makers to concede such right.

[109] *Id., passim.*

It still is unclear whether the grave difficulties attending this relative anarchy in exploitation will be resolved by the recent agreement directed at that end. The details of the Convention of the Conservation of the Living Resources of the Sea, adopted at Geneva in 1958, are not here relevant, and it suffices to note that the important provisions of this treaty seek both to allocate competence to coastal and non-coastal states to prescribe conservation regulations and to provide machinery for third-party settlement of disputes over such asserted competence. No experience has been possible as yet with the operation of these provisions since the treaty is not yet in force, and observers vary considerably in assessing its effectiveness in moderating, or avoiding entirely, the bitter disputes so frequently erupting over access to fishery resources. Some express the sanguine view that the 1958 Convention provides the necessary objective standards to which states can look to obtain relief. Others are less than optimistic on this score and call attention to a major omission from the 1958 Convention, namely the absence of any criteria for allocating a common resource that, by hypothesis, must be placed under a regime of limited exploitation. In this view, it does not seem likely that major disputes over division of a resource can be avoided by an agreement that seems to ignore that problem entirely. Whatever the accuracy of these opposing prognoses, observers should keep the situations supposedly subject to this agreement under close appraisal.

As with mineral resources, the problems for the future are whether principles developed in the past, including the recent 1958 treaty, may serve community policies in fishery exploitation under new conditions and, if the inherited prescriptions are inadequate to meet emerging needs, what practicable and desirable alternatives can be devised.

An assessment of experience indicates that one of the major neglected areas of inquiry has been the structure and functioning of the established fishery conservation organizations.[110] It has, of course, long been evident that unrestrained access to marine fisheries might create special problems for those engaged in exploita-

---

[110] Apparently the only systematic study is SWYGARD, THE INTERNATIONAL HALIBUT AND SOCKEYE SALMON FISHERIES COMMISSIONS: A STUDY IN INTERNATIONAL ADMINISTRATION (Ph.D. Thesis, University of Washington, 1948). Because the Salmon Commission was just beginning operations, Professor Swygard's inquiry centers upon the Halibut Commission, but within this scope the study is both superbly detailed and comprehensive.

tion. For a very long time, and that time is not entirely behind us, the critical problems for conservation regimes were thought to be those of preserving from complete extinction, the animal resource that was being exploited, and of maintaining the greatest physical yield that the particular resource could be thought to sustain on a year-to-year basis.[111] The focus in such efforts was, at least formally and perhaps also effectively, upon the means by which these objectives could be reached. In more recent times, these objectives have been criticized as being too limited, as over-emphasizing the biological condition of the resource to the exclusion of other considerations; and recommendations are increasingly offered that more sophisticated objectives must be conceived so that the entire social context of fishery exploitation can be taken into account in regulating access to the resources.[112] In whatever way the objectives have been expressed, states have had recourse to special organizations by which their aims have been sought. It appears to be worthwhile, if more effective efforts at management are to be made in the future when increased pressure on international fishery resources seems virtually inevitable, to undertake detailed inquiry into the structure and functioning of these beginning endeavors at regulating international resources. The object of such inquiry, as with any legal study, is to attempt to clarify goals, to observe trends in decision, to identify factors affecting decisions, to appraise the impact of decision in terms of the fulfilment of goals, and to offer recommendations to maximize the chances of achieving goals.

In organizing such an inquiry, observations of detail about a particular organization should be made in ways that permit a comparison with other groups over an extended period. One particular scheme, adapted from another study into the use of enterprisory organizations in the development of outer space, appears in the following outline.[113] In slight departure from outline form, brief statements or questions are included to indicate possible direction of inquiry into past experience.

[111] *Id.* at 4; Van Cleve & Johnson, *Management of the High Seas Fisheries of the Northeastern Pacific* 24–25 (U. of Wash. Pub. in Fisheries, New Series, Vol. II, No. 2, 1963).

[112] See sources cited in previous footnote and literature there cited.

[113] McDougal, Lasswell & Vlasic, *op. cit. supra* note 68, ch. 8.

a) *Features of Internal Constitutive Process*

(1) *Establishment of the Organization*

(a) *Constitutive Grant of Capacity*

The grant of legal capacity is not unusual even for international organizations, and it is of interest whether the charters of the fishery conservation bodies contain provisions for this and, if so, whether the form of stipulation is general or specific. It is possible that provision might be made for subjection to the local law of a member either by incorporation or by subjection to its supervision.

A separate but related question is whether occasion has arisen for non-members to recognize the capacity of the organization or to refuse to do so, either with respect to the "internal affairs" of the group or to relations with non-members.

(b) *Membership*

It may be useful, especially in comparing various organizations, to observe whether original membership in a group is dependent upon exploitation of a particular area or a particular resource and to note the varying effects upon identity of members. Additionally, membership may be limited to states alone or widened to include other entities. On occasion, degrees of association are established with other entities admitted to one of these categories. Subsequent members may be subjected to different qualifications and sometimes provision is made for original members to later assume a different status.

Termination of membership may be critical, and it is important to inquire into provisions for withdrawal, suspension, and expulsion, particularly examining both the conditions and limitations under which such actions can be taken and the procedures employed.

(2) *Structure of Organization*

The principal inquiry here is into the internal bodies or organs, their composition and method of establishment. It might be especially useful to note specific qualifications for membership in particular internal bodies. Revealing insight could also be possible by investigating the identifications of individuals serving on the component organs, i.e., whether they are industry representatives, government scientists, trade unionists, lawyers (and principal clients), or affiliated with a university. Effort should be made to analyze in terms of skill as well as interest categories.

Within a particular organ it is of interest whether particular states are afforded any special position with respect to certain kinds of decisions, as, for example, if members especially affected by a decision are granted a special competence with respect to that decision.

A decentralization of function may be sought as a means of engaging unique interests of some members, as, for example, the use of panels for geographical subareas by the Northwest Atlantic Fisheries Commission. Experience with this device should be carefully appraised for the contexts in which it has been found useful.

Obviously attention should be devoted to changes that occur in structure through time, including the addition or elimination of various organs and committees.

(3) *Objectives*

Special attention to this aspect of the constitutive process is justified since the efficacy and desirability of the objectives of established organizations should be subject to constant appraisal. Moreover, there appear to be substantial differences of opinion about the appropriate goals of marine conservation. For these reasons, if none other, scholarly inquiry should not only note the general and specific statements of formal objectives but also seek to discover the goals sought in effective operations. Where there appears to be a discrepancy in formal and effective objectives, investigation can then proceed to examination of conditioning factors.

(4) *Bases of Power*

It is unlikely that study will disclose that substantial assets have been conferred upon conservation organizations, but it is nevertheless of considerable importance to determine how the values at the disposal of the group are controlled by internal organs. The questions here are: who within the organization controls the wealth,

81

enlightenment, skill, loyalties, and other assets; and how is such control exercised.

(5) *Strategies*

The most important inquiry here relates to the allocation of authority within the group over diplomatic, ideological, and economic strategies. For appropriate emphasis in connection with diplomatic strategy, separate attention could be given to the voting provisions and practices of the organization, including provisions for weighted voting, the criteria for determining weight, the kinds of questions on which votes are weighted, the majority needed for various types of decisions, and the varying effect to be given to different types of decisions.

(6) *Outcomes*

Although it would be surprising if these international organizations were granted any comprehensive competence to make decisions, especially in the prescription and application of policy, useful analysis would extend to discovery of the internal distribution of such competences as are conferred. It seems probable that intelligence-serving is the single most important function of these groups, and comparative study to determine who performs this function might lead to valuable generalizations to add to those already advanced by observers.

(7) *Modification and Termination*

The potentially drastic impact upon fisheries from recent developments in scientific research and technology may make it imperative to make careful provision for amending the instrument establishing the conservation regime and for terminating the entire enterprise. Previous experience in this regard should be examined for the aid it may give future endeavors.

b). *External Interactions*

(1) *Participation*

A useful indicator of the scope of participation by these organizations in the more general constitutive process is to be found in their interaction with other participants. Nation-states, especially members, are most noticeable, but relationships with other entities are probably of no less importance. The international governmental organization, because of its pivotal role in intelligence-serving as a global enterprise, occupies a most critical position in interactions with these less universal marine conservation bodies. Even private groups and individuals are, in sum, virtually as important as states in terms of their interactions with conservation organizations.

(2) *Situations*

(a) *Geographical*

Sometimes states establish a conservation regime designed to operate in a particular part of the sea. Provisions for this purpose, and the assumptions underlying them, should be noted. In addition, it can be important to observe whether any limitations are placed upon access by the organization to particular ocean areas. Generally speaking, territorial waters of member states are excluded from permissible access by conservation organizations, though other areas of claimed exclusive fishing rights have not been. It remains to be seen whether the recent tendencies toward exclusive fishing zones beyond the territorial sea have impact on conservation activities.

(b) *Structures of Authority*

The matter for study under this heading includes the provisions and practices concerning access to the decision processes of other participants. With respect to member states, it is probable that most attention should be directed to intelligence and recommending functions. In addition to assessing the situation in regard to non-member states, note should be taken of provisions for co-ordination of activities with other international governmental groups, such as joint research work, interchange of observers, and exchange of information and advice.

Special care should be taken in observing relations between the conservation organizations and non-governmental groups. Frequently, the charter provides for the appointment of advisory groups or committees; and interest here centers upon the exact functions

83

performed by such advisers, their terms of reference, the composition of the group, and the degree of influence they possess. Among other outside groups, relations with affected elements in the community are noteworthy, such as the various segments of the fishing industry and associated industries.

A final point for inquiry slightly alters the focus, examining access by other groups to the organization, including those mentioned above. Access by communications media merits particular attention in view of the suspicion that conservation organizations have deliberately sought to operate free of consequential public scrutiny of their activities.

(3) *Acquisition and Control of Base Values*

(a) *Formal Authority*

The reference is to the specific competences that the states concerned have agreed to confer upon the organization. In addition, examination of the charter provisions and subsequent practice should include the privileges and immunities, if any, of the personnel and resources belonging to the organization.

(b) *Effective Power*

Financial underpinning of the organization is a fundamental component of effective power. Study should disclose the various sources of funds, the methods for deciding allocation of expenses, the criteria for determining obligation, the methods to be used in collection, and the sanctions available for assuring collection.

(4) *Strategies*

Focus here is, again both upon provisions of the charter authorizing the organization to engage in specific strategies vis-à-vis other participants and upon the applications of these provisions in practice. The nature of the conservation organizations is such that diplomatic and ideological strategies may be most significant. In connection with the latter, it would be of particular interest to discover the nature and scope of efforts, if any, to communicate with mass audiences and with special segments of the public, such as labor unions, industry groups, and scientific organizations.

(5) *Outcomes*

A most vital task involves detailed scrutiny of the charter provisions for, and the implementation of, performance of the decision functions of intelligence, recommendation, prescription, invocation, application, appraisal, and termination. With respect to each of these, the broad inquiry is: who, seeking what goals, has done what, under what conditions, utilizing what base values, pursuing what strategies, with what effects?

(6) *Effects*

Effort should be made to discover what long range impact the organization has had upon the values of all participants.

5. *Regulation of Shared Use*

The inherited prescriptions available for regulating sharable uses of the sea are not conspicuously available. It seems apparent that both decision-making structures and substantive policies and principles will have to be created to meet the new problems. As indicated above, certain structures of authority for decision-making are now established that may be put to use, but they are not now afforded any comprehensive competence and will have to be reconstituted if new difficulties in shared use are to be met properly.

CONCLUSION

However misguided the foregoing speculation about the concrete shape of future controversies, new sources of dispute probably will emerge from conflicting claims over the ocean and its resources. Assuming that it is useful to anticipate these possibilities, an important question concerns the steps that influential participants can take to avoid or minimize seriously disruptive conflict. Reference can be made to what is generally the most effective power holder, the nation-state, both as individual actor and as member of an alliance or coalition.

Of immediate interest are the alternatives either available to the United States or now being undertaken. The first measure that comes to mind, one indispensable to other efforts aimed at avoiding anticipated difficulties, is, of course, that of undertaking the necessary studies for determining as carefully as possible the inclusive and exclusive interests that states generally, and the United States in particular, should seek in interactions with others. Fortunately, individuals in the government and interested private groups seem fully aware of this need and are sponsoring meaningful action. The first session of the Eighty-ninth Congress has had before it legislation embodying provision for studies of certain aspects of sea law,[114] reflecting the concern expressed by individual congressmen that research be undertaken as a means of avoiding disputes.[115] Among private groups, the Committee on Oceanography of the National Academy of Sciences has established the Panel on Law, Uses of the Sea and Technology, which is charged with examination of important problems. The academic community, too, has begun to take initiatives in promoting inquiry into the law of the sea. The University of Rhode Island, for example, through its depart-ments of oceanography and geography has created a Law of the Sea Institute that seeks, among other goals, to facilitate communica-tion among scientists, engineers, businessmen, and lawyers con-cerned with sea problems. Members of the faculty of the University of Washington have been notably active in interdisciplinary studies in fishing aspects of ocean exploitation.[116]

Use of diplomatic strategies would gain in effectiveness and, perhaps, acquire impetus from the studies and actions just men-tioned. Indeed, one area of fruitful inquiry, perhaps urgently needed, is that of examining the process of multilateral agreement-making by which the world community has sought to reach explicit agree-ment on the law of the sea. Experienced individual participants in international negotiations and observers of this process warn that, from an American perspective, multilateral diplomatic initiatives for agreement about phases of ocean exploitation must be under-taken cautiously and that careful attention must be devoted to a considerable range of problems if general agreement is sought only on one of them. It is said that the 1958 Geneva Conference on the Law of the Sea dealt with issues other than those of primary inter-est to the United States and that it was necessary to take and de-

---

[114] H. R. 5175, introduced by Congressman Lennon, provides for a study of the legal problems of management use, and control of the natural resources of the oceans and ocean bed. With respect to this legislation, the State Department is reported to have stated that it was unaware of the need for any such study from the stand-point of international law or relations. See U.S. HOUSE OF REP., *Legislative Calen-dar*, Committee on Merchant Marine and Fisheries, June 15, 1965, p. 49. In contrast the Office of Science and Technology is reported to have observed that such studies "could well serve to consolidate the applicable existing federal and international statutes and may highlight unsuspected legal programs [*sic*] arising from new activities of the national oceanographic program" *(Ibid)*.

[115] Statement of Congressman Hanna in *Hearings, supra* note 9, at 89.

[116] See, e.g., Van Cleve & Johnson, *Supra* note 111; Royce *et. al., Salmon Gear Limitation in Northern Washington Waters* (U. of Wash. Pub. in Fisheries, New Series, Vol. II, No. 1, 1963); Biological and Economic Aspects of Fisheries Manage-ment (Crutchfield ed. 1959).

fend a position on these issues even though the real American interest was focused on the need for agreement on other problems. Assuming, for present purposes, the validity of this view of the events at Geneva in 1958, it could be very helpful to study the Geneva conferences from this perspective to learn what can be done to create more favorable conditions for resolving widely controverted issues. It does not seem necessary to conclude that the Geneva experience must inevitably be repeated and that modification of the process is impossible or not worth the effort. The problem thus posed is that of planning the presentation of proposals and their consideration and disposition in ways that permit focus on relatively narrow issues involving selected problems. The suggestion is that study of the Geneva Conference and the events leading to it may provide important clues to improved diplomatic strategies.

It might be helpful in this connection to recall that important agreements about international resources can be reached without the participation of every single state in the world. For example, radioactive waste disposal and fishery problems might be handled with most efficiency in less than universal arenas.

Beyond implementation of desirable policies through carefully designed and executed negotiations on selected problems—selected, it may be emphasized, without awaiting the confrontation of a crisis—the United States can utilize a variety of other assets in a program that hopefully will help to avoid serious conflicts over the ocean. The available store of enlightenment would seem to be especially valuable and might be managed in several relevant ways. One major, relatively untapped alternative would seek to harness persons with specialized skills to shed light on anticipated problems. The economic aspects of fishery exploitation have attracted concern only within recent years, and the level of this concern is probably still inadequate for the scope of the problem. Whatever the merits attending positions adopted by contestants in argumentation about appropriate objectives for management of fisheries, a major program of economic study could provide information essential to resolution, or at least clarification, of disputes. The value of investigation into these economic aspects of exploitation is, of course, not limited to fishery resources in which the United States has a direct interest. For numerous reasons, study of this type should probably proceed under the auspices of international institutions.

Conclusion

The influence of a particular state upon decision outcomes dealing with specific legal issues may be intimately affected by the timing, as well as the substantive content, of its own initial claims about authority. It may be recalled, for example, that the United States Proclamation concerning the continental shelf had an undeniable impact on the ultimate decision by the general community about allocation of resources in this area. On one of the substantive problems alluded to above, the United States may again be in a position to play a critical role through assertion of unilateral claim or, at least, influential pronouncement. As noted above, the mining of ocean floor surficial deposits may become a reality in the foreseeable future. From present indications, it seems most likely that United States nationals will take the lead in entering upon this form of exploitation and that the United States government will be called upon to take a position about the scope and substantive details of claims to access. The opportunity thus presented is that of taking the lead in establishing a pattern of responsibility and restraint in the assertion of claim to newly available resources. To be sure, past experience has been that restraint in assertion of claim has not prevented others from making extravagant demands. Nonetheless it merits emphasis that these demands, though still not wholly effectively refuted, have never commanded wide assent and, indeed, have been categorically rejected by most states. At the very least, it seems evident that the United States could, by suitably limited claim or announced position, promote policies directed at maximizing inclusive benefit from the vast storehouse of resources in and under the sea.

The latter point can be generalized, of course, though perhaps not too helpfully, to the effect that all assertions of claim regarding access to, and authority over, the oceans should be designed to serve the common interests of states both inclusive and exclusive. The task of appropriate specification of such interests, and their accommodation, is a separate task not assayed here.

Turning the focus of attention from the state as an individual participant to the state in the wider setting of an alliance or coalition may disclose new requirements for appraisal and action. Specifically it may be time for members to devote systematic attention to the impact on relations with each other of scientific and other developments involving the ocean. Already, of course, stress from intra-alliance conflicts over fishery exploitation has occasioned multilateral efforts at alleviation. But these were more or less familiar controversies, with backgrounds as ancient as the fishing grounds themselves. The point now is that there may be new, perhaps unexpected, pressures from wholly new directions unless some effort is made at anticipation. Suggestive in this connection is the burgeoning activity in the North Sea directed at oil and gas exploration. Perhaps the discoveries there will be so immense that boundaries can be established in amicable fashion, but perhaps the resource may be less abundant so that locations of productive areas might engender serious divisiveness among allied states.

Valuable discoveries in the North Sea might have effects elsewhere too, as upon alliances in the Middle East. The Arab world now appears to be in some disarray, and the cessation of European dependence upon Middle East oil could conceivably add to the difficulties or, perhaps, even lessen them.

In the even wider perspective of relations between the highly industrialized states and the lesser developed, the discovery and exploitation of marine mineral resources may have important impact. A tendency toward reliance upon the raw materials exported by lesser developed states may cease or change direction, with unknown effects upon political relationships.

Within the Communist bloc, or blocs, where dissension is noticeable, relationships can be influenced by ocean developments. Earlier, for example, it was speculated that employment of submarines by Communist China could conceivably lend some enchantment to agreement by the United States and the Soviet Union on armament control.

In sum, it seems apparent that the protection of common interests calls for continued appraisal and study, by all participants, but particularly by the nation-state, of the processes of interaction, claim, and decision involving the ocean.

R